It's another Quality Book from CGP

This book is for anyone doing OCR Modular
GCSE Mathematics at Higher Level.

It contains lots of tricky questions designed
to make you sweat — because that's the only
way you'll get any better.

It's also got some daft bits in to try and make
the whole experience at least vaguely
entertaining for you.

What CGP is all about

Our sole aim here at CGP is to produce the highest quality
books — carefully written, immaculately presented and
dangerously close to being funny.

Then we work our socks off to get them
out to you — at the cheapest possible prices.

Contents

Module 8

Module 9

Module 10

Published by Coordination Group Publications Ltd.

Editors:
Tim Burne
Simon Little
Ali Palin

Contributors:
Gill Allen
Margaret Carr
Barbara Coleman
JE Dodds
Mark Haslam
John Lyons
C McLoughlin
Gordon Rutter
Claire Thompson
John Waller
Dave Williams
Phillip Wood

With thanks to Janet Dickinson *and*
Charley Darbishire *for the proofreading.*

ISBN: 978 1 84146 573 9

Groovy website: www.cgpbooks.co.uk

Printed by Elanders Hindson Ltd, Newcastle upon Tyne.
Clipart sources: CorelDRAW® and VECTOR.

MODULE 6

1

Rounding Numbers

With all these rounding methods, you need to identify the last digit — e.g. if you're rounding **23.41** to 1 decimal place the last digit is **4**. Then look at the next digit to the right. If it's 5 or more you round up, if it's 4 or less you round down.

Q1 Round these numbers to the required number of decimal places:

a) 62.1935 (1 dp)   **d)** 19.624328 (5 dp)

b) 62.1935 (2 dp)   **e)** 6.2999 (3 dp)

c) 62.1935 (3 dp)   **f)** π (3 dp)

Q2 Round these numbers to the required number of significant figures.

a) 1329.62 (3 SF)   **d)** 120 (1 SF)

b) 1329.62 (4 SF)   **e)** 0.024687 (1 SF)

c) 1329.62 (5 SF)   **f)** 0.024687 (4 SF)

Remember — the first significant figure is the first digit which isn't zero.

Q3 K = 456.9873
Write K correct to:

a) one decimal place   **d)** three significant figures

b) two decimal places   **e)** two significant figures

c) three decimal places   **f)** one significant figure.

Q4 Calculate the square root of 8. Write your answer to two decimal places.

Q5 Calculate, giving your answers to a sensible degree of accuracy:

a) $\dfrac{42.65 \times 0.9863}{24.6 \times 2.43}$ **b)** $\dfrac{13.63 + 7.22}{13.63 - 7.22}$

Q6 The great racing driver Speedy Wheelman covered 234.65 miles during the course of one of his races. Give this distance correct to the nearest mile.

Q7 Pru measured the length of her bedroom as 2.345 metres. Give this measurement correct to the nearest centimetre.

Q8 At a golf club, a putting green is given as being 5 m long to the nearest metre. Give the range of values that the actual length of the green could be.

Calculator Questions

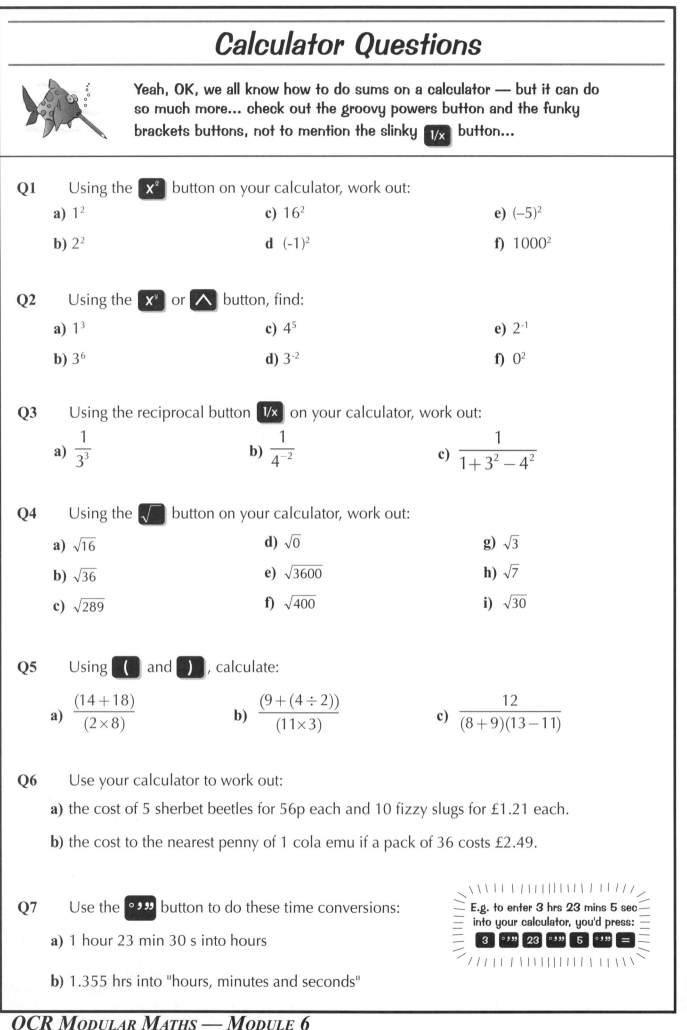

Yeah, OK, we all know how to do sums on a calculator — but it can do so much more... check out the groovy powers button and the funky brackets buttons, not to mention the slinky ▮1/x▮ button...

Q1 Using the ▮x²▮ button on your calculator, work out:

   a) 1^2 **c)** 16^2 **e)** $(-5)^2$

   b) 2^2 **d** $(-1)^2$ **f)** 1000^2

Q2 Using the ▮xʸ▮ or ▮∧▮ button, find:

   a) 1^3 **c)** 4^5 **e)** 2^{-1}

   b) 3^6 **d)** 3^{-2} **f)** 0^2

Q3 Using the reciprocal button ▮1/x▮ on your calculator, work out:

   a) $\dfrac{1}{3^3}$ **b)** $\dfrac{1}{4^{-2}}$ **c)** $\dfrac{1}{1+3^2-4^2}$

Q4 Using the ▮√▮ button on your calculator, work out:

   a) $\sqrt{16}$ **d)** $\sqrt{0}$ **g)** $\sqrt{3}$

   b) $\sqrt{36}$ **e)** $\sqrt{3600}$ **h)** $\sqrt{7}$

   c) $\sqrt{289}$ **f)** $\sqrt{400}$ **i)** $\sqrt{30}$

Q5 Using ▮(▮ and ▮)▮ , calculate:

   a) $\dfrac{(14+18)}{(2\times8)}$ **b)** $\dfrac{(9+(4\div2))}{(11\times3)}$ **c)** $\dfrac{12}{(8+9)(13-11)}$

Q6 Use your calculator to work out:

   a) the cost of 5 sherbet beetles for 56p each and 10 fizzy slugs for £1.21 each.

   b) the cost to the nearest penny of 1 cola emu if a pack of 36 costs £2.49.

Q7 Use the ▮°'"▮ button to do these time conversions:

E.g. to enter 3 hrs 23 mins 5 sec into your calculator, you'd press:
▮3▮ ▮°'"▮ ▮23▮ ▮°'"▮ ▮5▮ ▮°'"▮ ▮=▮

   a) 1 hour 23 min 30 s into hours

   b) 1.355 hrs into "hours, minutes and seconds"

Written Multiplication and Division

Time to test your multiplying and dividing skills without a calculator.
There are lots of methods — you need to <u>pick a method</u> you like and
<u>practise using it</u> on questions until it's as stress free as bungee jumping...

<u>NO CALCULATORS</u> for any of these questions on this page,

Q1 Use written methods to multiply the following:

a) 23 × 2   b) 225 × 3   c) 546 × 5   d) 126 × 14

e) 152 × 33   f) 413 × 26   g) 309 × 61   h) 847 × 53

Q2 Now use written methods to deal with these:

a) 834 ÷ 3   b) 645 ÷ 5   c) 702 ÷ 6

d) 1000 ÷ 8   e) 595 ÷ 17   f) 728 ÷ 13

g) 768 ÷ 16   h) 996 ÷ 24   i) 665 ÷ 14

Now let's try some slightly trickier questions involving decimals.

Q3 Now try these multiplications.

a) 6.2 × 4   b) 8.6 × 5

c) 4.75 × 3   d) 66.2 × 0.2

Count the number of d.p.s in the question
and put the same number into your answer.

e) 263 × 1.4   f) 2.52 × 0.13

Q4 Finally, try these divisions:

a) 27.2 ÷ 4   b) 31.8 ÷ 6   c) 52.15 ÷ 7

d) 7.36 ÷ 1.6   e) 91.2 ÷ 2.4   f) 37.8 ÷ 14

g) 2.6 ÷ 0.4   h) 3.6 ÷ 0.4   i) 156.8 ÷ 3.2

Ratios

Ratios compare quantities of the same kind — so if the units aren't mentioned, they've got to be the same in each bit of the ratio.

Q1 Write each of these ratios in its simplest form. The first one is done for you.
E.g. 16 to 4 becomes 4 : 1.

a) 4 to 6   **b)** 15 to 21   **c)** 14 to 42   **d)** 72 to 45

e) 24 cm to 36 cm   **f)** 350 g to 2 kg   **g)** 42p to £1.36

Watch out for ones like f) and g) — you need to make the units the same first.

Q2 The ratio of men to women at a football match was 11:4.
How many men were there if there were:

a) 2000 women?   **b)** 8460 women?

How many women were there if there were:

c) 22000 men?   **d)** 6820 men?

Q3 A recipe for Ozzy's Speciality Omelette serves 4 people and uses 3/4 pint of herbal tea.
How much herbal tea will be needed to make an omelette for:

a) 32 people?   **b)** 96 people?   **c)** 12 people?   **d)** 672 people?

Q4 Ozzy's Speciality Orange Smoothie is made by mixing orange juice and herbal tea in the ratio 7 : 1.

a) How much orange juice is needed to make 600 ml of smoothie?

b) How many ml of tea are needed to make 1 litre of smoothie?

c) If 200 ml of tea are used, how much smoothie will be made?

Q5 The plan of a house is drawn to a scale of 1 cm to 3 m.

a) Write this ratio in its simplest form.

b) How wide is a room that appears as 2 cm on the drawing?

c) How long will a 10 m hall look on the drawing?

Make sure you convert to the same units when you're working out the ratio.

Q6 I picked some strawberries after a few wet days. Some were nibbled by snails, some were mouldy and some fine. The ratio was 2:3:10 respectively. If 9 strawberries were mouldy how many:

a) were fine?

b) were not fine?

c) What fraction of the total amount were fine?

Fractions

A FRACTION IS A DECIMAL IS A PERCENTAGE —
they're all just different ways of saying "a bit of" something.

Q1 Change these fractions to decimals:

a) $\dfrac{1}{100}$ b) $\dfrac{3}{8}$ c) $\dfrac{2}{1000}$ d) $\dfrac{1}{3}$

Q2 Change these fractions to percentages:

a) $\dfrac{8}{100}$ b) $\dfrac{2}{40}$ c) $\dfrac{7}{8}$ d) $\dfrac{11}{30}$

Q3 Change these decimals to percentages:

a) 0.62   b) 0.02   c) 0.125   d) 0.987

Q4 Change these percentages to decimals:

a) 25%   b) 49%   c) 3%   d) 30%

Q5 Change these percentages to fractions:

a) 75%   b) 60%   c) 15%   d) 53%

Q6 Change these decimals to fractions:

a) 0.5   b) 0.8   c) 0.19   d) 0.25

Q7 Cancel down these fractions to express them in their simplest form.

a) 8/16   b) 24/32   c) 57/60   d) 45/72   e) 14/21   f) 150/600

Q8 There were 65 people at a jungle-themed party. 20% came dressed as Declan Donnelly, 2/5 came dressed as Ant McPartlin. Everyone else came dressed as Ant-eaters. How many people came as Ant-eaters?

Fractions

Fraction arithmetic becomes a nice stroll in the desert, once you've <u>learned the rules</u>:

MULTIPLYING — multiply top and bottom separately,
DIVIDING — invert the second fraction then treat like multiplication.
ADDING / SUBTRACTING — put over a common denominator,
then add / subtract the top line only.

Tip

No calculators for any of these questions...

Q9   Change these top-heavy fractions to mixed numbers:

\\\\\| | |||||||||| | |/|//
For some of the questions
below, you'll need to change the
mixed fractions into top-heavy
fractions at the start.
//|| | \\\\\\\\\\ | | |\\\

a) $\frac{3}{2}$ b) $\frac{7}{4}$ c) $\frac{8}{3}$

Change these mixed numbers to top-heavy fractions:

d) $2\frac{1}{2}$ e) $3\frac{1}{3}$ f) $1\frac{3}{5}$

Q10   Do these multiplications, giving the answers as fractions in their lowest terms:

a) $\frac{4}{3} \times \frac{3}{4}$ d) $2\frac{1}{2} \times \frac{3}{5}$

b) $\frac{2}{5} \times \frac{3}{4}$ e) $10\frac{2}{7} \times \frac{7}{9}$

c) $\frac{11}{9} \times \frac{6}{5}$ f) $2\frac{1}{6} \times 3\frac{1}{3}$

Q11   Now do these divisions, giving the answers in their lowest terms:

a) $\frac{1}{4} \div \frac{3}{8}$ d) $1\frac{1}{2} \div \frac{5}{12}$

b) $\frac{1}{9} \div \frac{2}{3}$ e) $10\frac{4}{5} \div \frac{9}{10}$

c) $\frac{15}{24} \div \frac{6}{5}$ f) $3\frac{7}{11} \div 1\frac{4}{11}$

Q12   Add the two fractions, giving your answer as a fraction in its lowest terms:

a) $\frac{7}{8} + \frac{3}{8}$ b) $\frac{1}{12} + \frac{3}{4}$ c) $\frac{1}{3} + \frac{3}{4}$

d) $1\frac{2}{5} + 2\frac{2}{3}$ e) $\frac{1}{6} + 4\frac{1}{3}$ f) $1\frac{3}{10} + \frac{2}{5}$

Q13   Evaluate, giving your answer as a fraction in its lowest terms:

a) $\frac{11}{4} - \frac{2}{3}$ b) $10 - \frac{2}{5}$ c) $1\frac{3}{4} - 1\frac{1}{5}$

d) $4\frac{2}{3} - \frac{7}{9}$ e) $3\frac{1}{2} - \frac{2}{3}$ f) $8 - \frac{1}{8}$

Algebra

With night comes day, with dark comes light, and with <u>multiplying out brackets</u> comes <u>putting them back in again</u>...

Q1 Multiply out the brackets and simplify if possible.

> Simplifying means <u>collecting like terms</u>.
> E.g. $x + 3 + 2x - 2 = 3x - 1$.

a) $2(x + y)$

b) $4(x - 3)$

c) $8(x^2 + 2)$

d) $-2(x + 5)$

e) $-(y - 2)$

f) $x(y + 2)$

g) $x(x + y + z)$

h) $8(a + b) + 2(a + 2b)$

i) $4(x + y - z)$

j) $x(x + 5)$

k) $-3(x - 2)$

l) $7(a + b) + 2(a + b)$

m) $3(a + 2b) - 2(2a + b)$

n) $4(x - 2) - 2(x - 1)$

o) $14(2m - n) + 2(3n - 6m)$

p) $3(2 + ab) + 5(1 - ab)$

q) $4(x - 2y) - (5 + x - 2y)$

r) $a - 4(a + b)$

Q2 Factorise the expressions below. Each has 4 as a common factor.

a) $4x + 8$

b) $12 - 8x$

c) $4 - 16x$

d) $4x^2 + 64$

Q3 Factorise the expressions below. Each has 7 as a common factor.

a) $21 - 7x$

b) $28x + 7$

c) $14 + 21x$

d) $35x^2 - 14$

Q4 Factorise the expressions below. Each has a^2 as a common factor.

a) $a^2b + a^2c$

b) $5a^2 + 13a^2b$

c) $2a^2b + 3a^2c$

d) $a^3 + a^2y^2$

Q5 Factorise the expressions below.

a) $2x + 4$

b) $3x + 12$

c) $24 + 12x$

d) $16x + 4y$

e) $3x + 15$

f) $30 + 10x$

g) $2x + x^2$

h) $3a + 6b^2$

i) $xyz - x^2$

j) $8y^2 - 5xy^2$

k) $2t + 7t^2$

l) $pqr^2 + 2r$

> First look for any numbers the terms have in common, then look for letters.

Equations and Formulas

Q1   Solve these equations:

a) $4x = 20$ **e)** $x + 3 = 11$ **i)** $2x + 1 = 7$

b) $2z = -18$ **f)** $23 = x + 19$ **j)** $54 = 7x + 5$

c) $\dfrac{x}{2} = 22$ **g)** $3x + 2 = 14$ **k)** $5x - 4 = 31$

d) $8 = \dfrac{a}{5}$ **h)** $\dfrac{8 + 6x}{5} = 10$ **l)** $-61 = 20 - 3x$

Q2   Now solve the following:

a) $3(2x + 1) = 27$ **d)** $2(4x + 1) + x = 56$

b) $5x + 3 = 2x + 15$ **e)** $2(x + 7) = 6x - 10$

c) $3x + 5 = 2(4x - 10)$ **f)** $-(x + 2) = 2(x + 2)$

**Now for some practice at substituting into formulas.
Remember to use BODMAS to get the order of operations right.**

Q3   If $x = 3$ and $y = 6$ find the value of the following expressions.

a) $x + 2y$ **c)** $2x^2$ **e)** $x^2 + 5$

b) $2x \div y$ **d)** $2y^2$ **f)** $2x^3 - 3$

Q4   Work out the value of $4y^2 + y^3$ when:

a) $y = 2$ **b)** $y = -2$

Q5   Using the formula $z = (x - 10)^2$, find the value of z when:

a) $x = 20$ **b)** $x = -1$ **c)** $x = -10$

Q6   The volume of a sphere is found using the formula $\frac{4}{3}\pi r^3$, where r is the radius of the sphere. Find (to 1 d.p.) the volume of a sphere with a radius of:

a) 2 cm   **b)** 5 cm

Drawing Graphs from Equations

Top tip Always check your graph is a <u>dead straight line</u>. If it's not, work out the offending y-value again and check you've plotted it correctly. And watch out for the equations that need to be <u>rearranged</u> before you start.

Q1 On a copy of the diagram:

a) Draw and label the line y = x.

b) Draw and label the line y = -x.

c) Draw the line x = -3.

d) Draw the line y = -2.

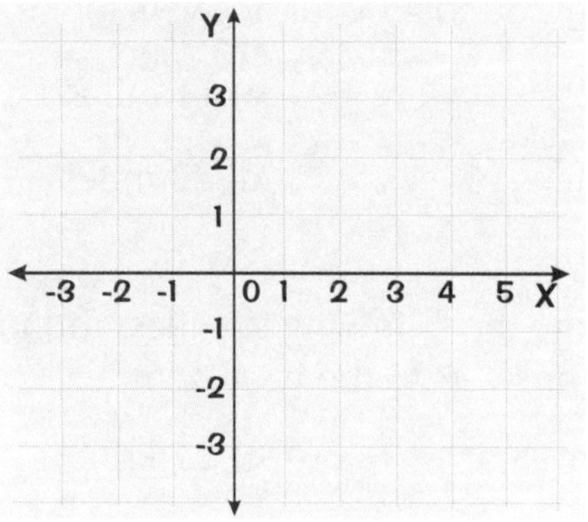

Q2 On graph paper, draw axes with x from 0 to 8 and y from 0 to 14.

Q3 a) Complete the table of values for y = x + 1.

b) Use the table of values to draw the graph of y = x + 1 on your axes.

x	0	1	2	3	4	5	6
y	1			4			

Q4 a) Complete the table of values for y + x = 10, by first rearranging the equation.

b) Use the table of values to draw the graph of y + x = 10 on your axes.

x	0	1	2	3	4	5	6
y	10				6		

Q5 a) Fill in the table for y − 2x = 2, using values of x from 0 to 6.

b) Use the table of values to draw the graph of y − 2x = 2 on your axes.

x							
y							

Q6 Draw the following graphs for values of x between 0 and 6:

a) y = 5 − x

b) y = 3x − 3

Draw up your own table of values for each of these. Once you've filled in the table, you'll know what number the y-axis needs to go up to.

c) y = ½x + 3

Interpreting Graphs

A whole page of graph questions and the good news is there's not a single point to be plotted. These questions are about <u>understanding</u> what the graphs are showing.

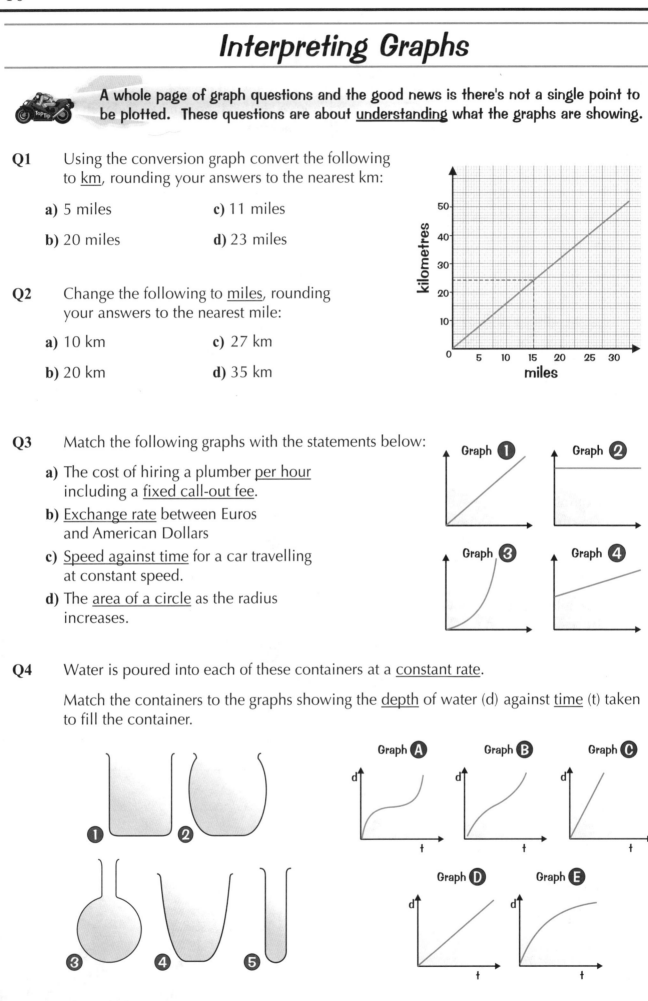

Q1 Using the conversion graph convert the following to <u>km</u>, rounding your answers to the nearest km:

a) 5 miles   **c)** 11 miles

b) 20 miles   **d)** 23 miles

Q2 Change the following to <u>miles</u>, rounding your answers to the nearest mile:

a) 10 km   **c)** 27 km

b) 20 km   **d)** 35 km

Q3 Match the following graphs with the statements below:

a) The cost of hiring a plumber <u>per hour</u> including a <u>fixed call-out fee</u>.

b) <u>Exchange rate</u> between Euros and American Dollars

c) <u>Speed against time</u> for a car travelling at constant speed.

d) The <u>area of a circle</u> as the radius increases.

Q4 Water is poured into each of these containers at a <u>constant rate</u>.

Match the containers to the graphs showing the <u>depth</u> of water (d) against <u>time</u> (t) taken to fill the container.

Polygons

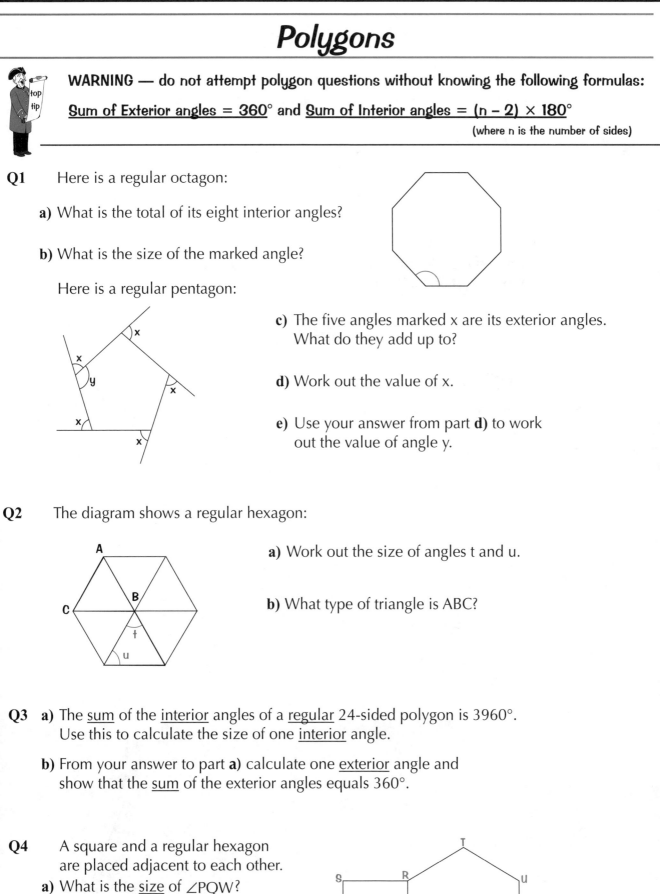

Q1 Here is a regular octagon:

a) What is the total of its eight interior angles?

b) What is the size of the marked angle?

Here is a regular pentagon:

c) The five angles marked x are its exterior angles. What do they add up to?

d) Work out the value of x.

e) Use your answer from part **d)** to work out the value of angle y.

Q2 The diagram shows a regular hexagon:

a) Work out the size of angles t and u.

b) What type of triangle is ABC?

Q3 a) The <u>sum</u> of the <u>interior</u> angles of a <u>regular</u> 24-sided polygon is 3960°. Use this to calculate the size of one <u>interior</u> angle.

b) From your answer to part **a)** calculate one <u>exterior</u> angle and show that the <u>sum</u> of the exterior angles equals 360°.

Q4 A square and a regular hexagon are placed adjacent to each other.
a) What is the <u>size</u> of ∠PQW?
b) What is the <u>size</u> of ∠PRW?
c) How many sides has the <u>regular</u> polygon that has ∠PQW as one of its interior angles?

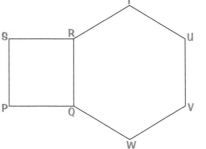

Parallel Lines

Once you know the <u>three angle rules</u> for parallel lines, there's no end to the amount of angle fun you can have — you'll see what I mean...

c = f and d = e — Alternate angles

a = e, c = g, b = f and d = h — Corresponding angles

d + f = 180°, c + e = 180° — Supplementary angles

Q1 Find the sizes of the angles marked by letters in these diagrams.
Write down what sort of angle each one is. *i.e. alternate, corresponding or supplementary*

NOT DRAWN TO SCALE

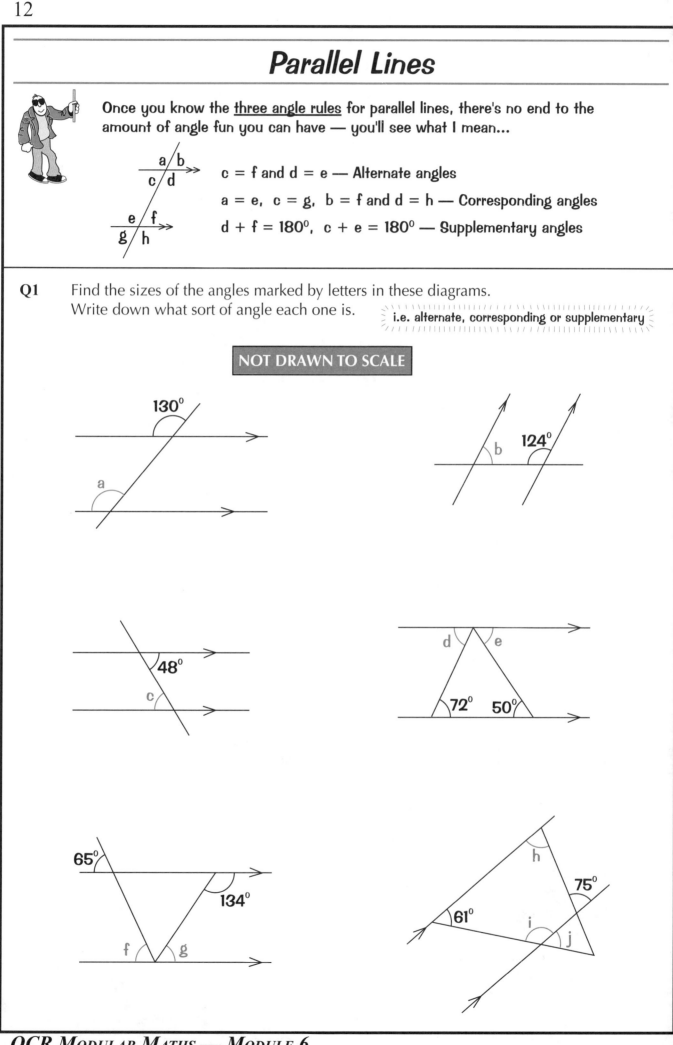

Perimeter and Area

The 'big blob method' for finding perimeters is like an old friend — it never lets you down. Put a blob at one corner, then go round adding up the sides till you're back at the blob.

Q1 Work out the perimeters of the following shapes:

a) Symmetrical Five Sided Shape

b) Symmetrical Four Sided Shape

c)

d)

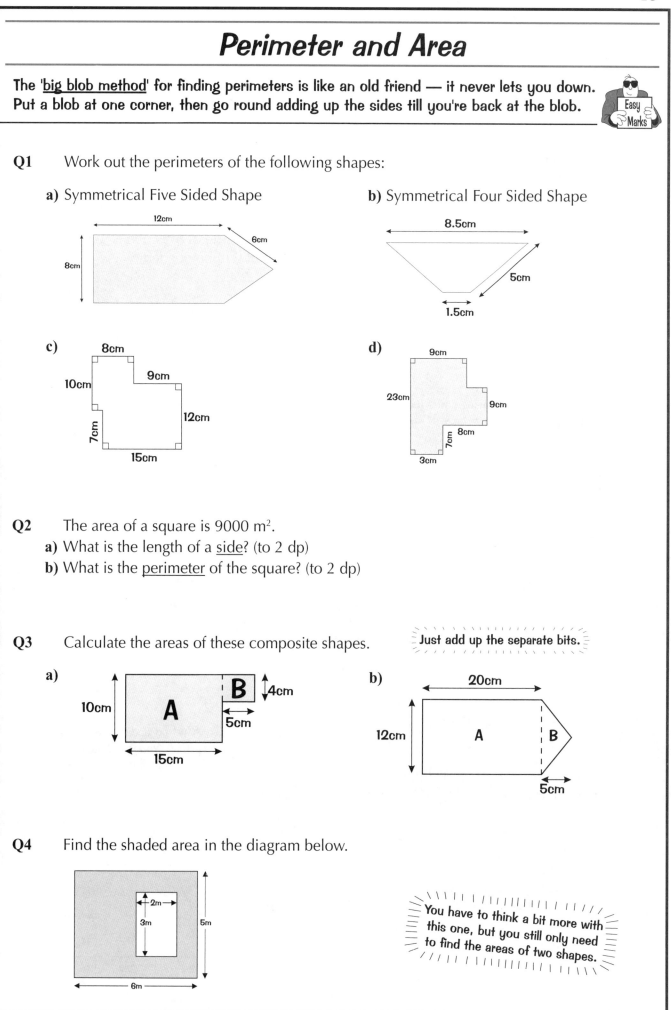

Q2 The area of a square is 9000 m².
a) What is the length of a side? (to 2 dp)
b) What is the perimeter of the square? (to 2 dp)

Q3 Calculate the areas of these composite shapes.

Just add up the separate bits.

a)

b)

Q4 Find the shaded area in the diagram below.

You have to think a bit more with this one, but you still only need to find the areas of two shapes.

Areas

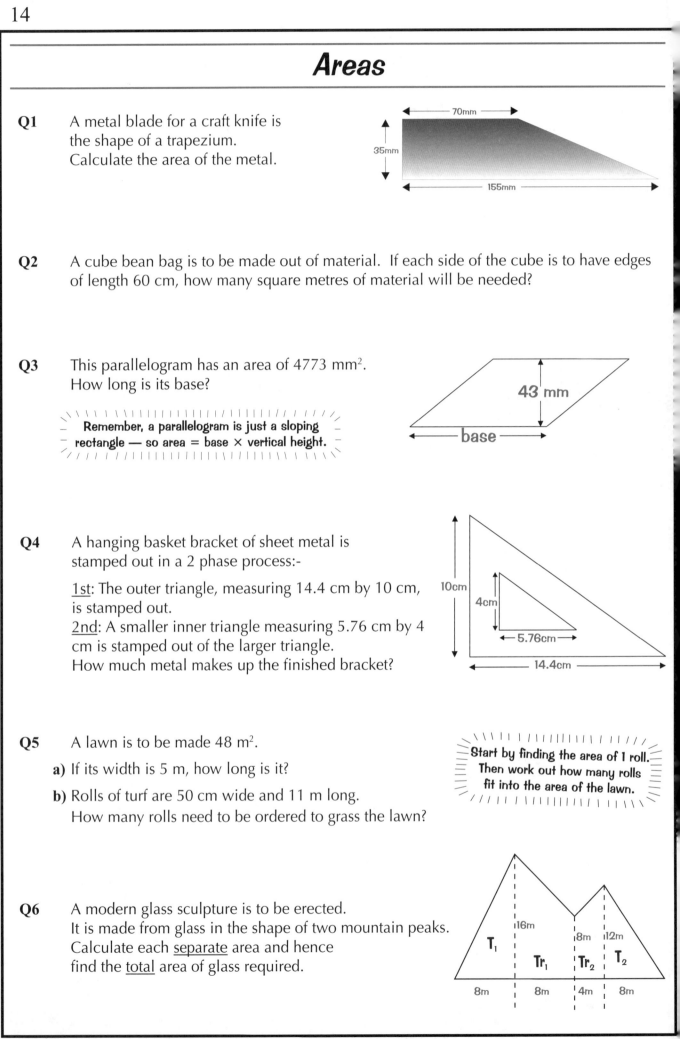

Q1   A metal blade for a craft knife is
the shape of a trapezium.
Calculate the area of the metal.

Q2   A cube bean bag is to be made out of material. If each side of the cube is to have edges
of length 60 cm, how many square metres of material will be needed?

Q3   This parallelogram has an area of 4773 mm².
How long is its base?

Remember, a parallelogram is just a sloping
rectangle — so area = base × vertical height.

Q4   A hanging basket bracket of sheet metal is
stamped out in a 2 phase process:-

1st: The outer triangle, measuring 14.4 cm by 10 cm,
is stamped out.
2nd: A smaller inner triangle measuring 5.76 cm by 4
cm is stamped out of the larger triangle.
How much metal makes up the finished bracket?

Q5   A lawn is to be made 48 m².

a) If its width is 5 m, how long is it?

b) Rolls of turf are 50 cm wide and 11 m long.
How many rolls need to be ordered to grass the lawn?

Start by finding the area of 1 roll.
Then work out how many rolls
fit into the area of the lawn.

Q6   A modern glass sculpture is to be erected.
It is made from glass in the shape of two mountain peaks.
Calculate each <u>separate</u> area and hence
find the <u>total</u> area of glass required.

The Circle Formulas

Don't worry about that π bit — it just stands for the number **3.14159...** Sometimes you'll be told to round it off to **3** or **3.14.** If not, just use the π button on your calculator.

Q1   A plant is in a pot. The radius of the top of the pot is 4.5 cm. Calculate the circumference of the top of the pot.

Circumference = 2πr

Q2   The circumference of a circle is 195 cm. Calculate its diameter correct to 3 s.f.

Q3   Calculate the area of each circle. Give your answers to 3 sig. figs.

a)

11cm

b)

2.5cm

Area of circle = πr²

c) A circle of diameter 28 cm.

Q4   Find the area of one face of a 10p coin, radius 1.2 cm. Give your answer correct to 3 s.f.

Q5   This circular pond has a circular path around it. The radius of the pond is 72 m and the path is 2 m wide. Calculate to the nearest whole number:

a) the area of the pond

b) the area of the path

path

pond

Q6   A circular table has an area of 7800 cm². Find the diameter of the table to 3 s.f.

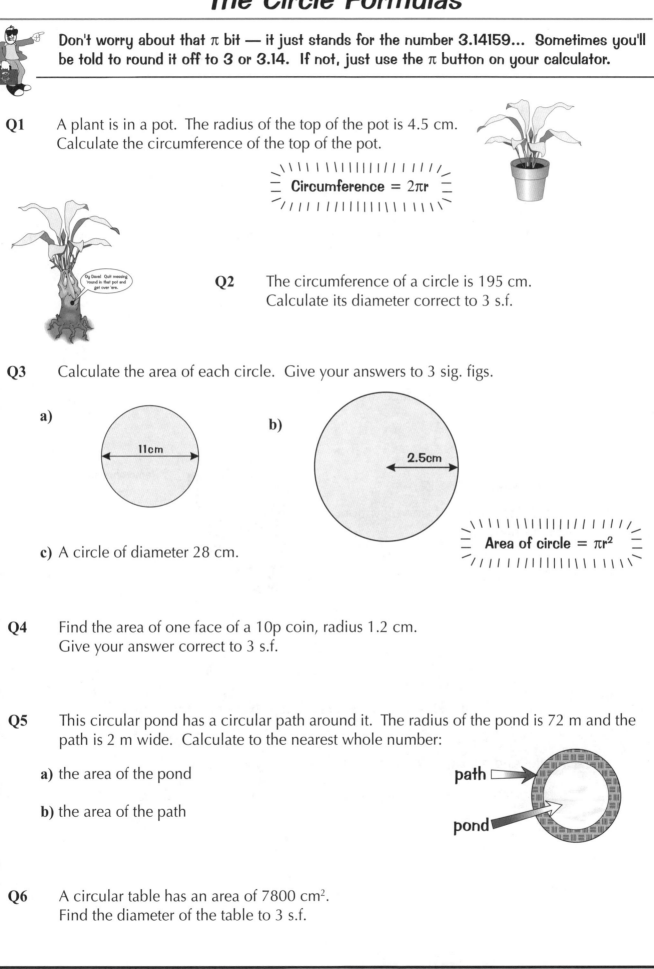

Solids, Nets and Constructions

A net is just a solid shape folded out flat. And what's more, the <u>area</u> of the net is the <u>surface area</u> of the solid. Pretty obvious really, but very useful...

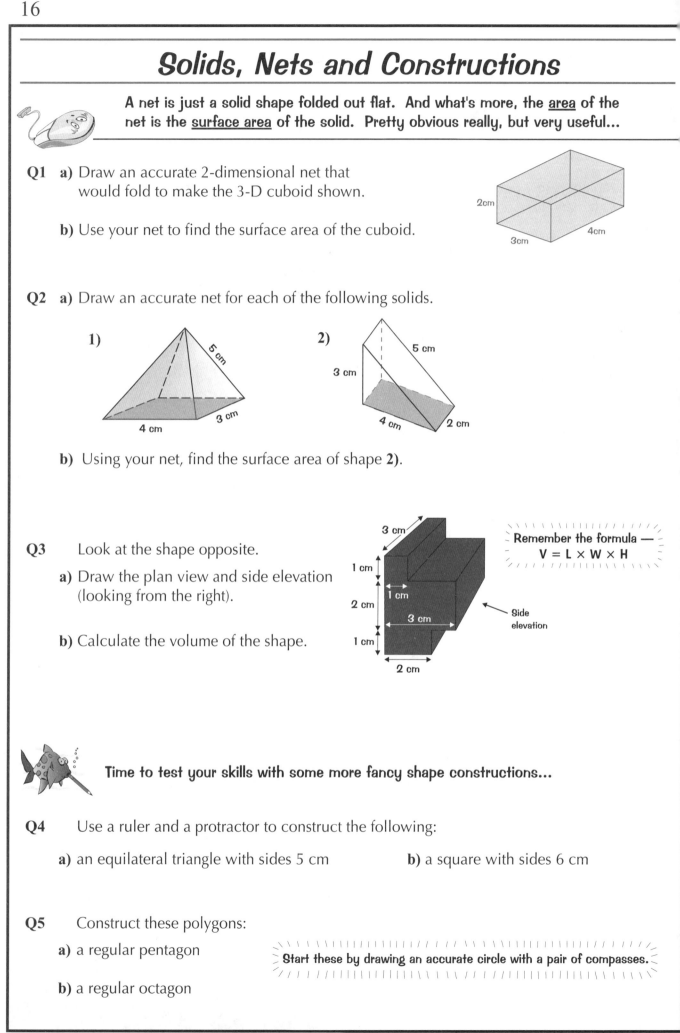

Q1 **a)** Draw an accurate 2-dimensional net that would fold to make the 3-D cuboid shown.

b) Use your net to find the surface area of the cuboid.

2cm
3cm
4cm

Q2 **a)** Draw an accurate net for each of the following solids.

1)
5 cm
4 cm
3 cm

2)
5 cm
3 cm
4 cm
2 cm

b) Using your net, find the surface area of shape **2)**.

Q3 Look at the shape opposite.

a) Draw the plan view and side elevation (looking from the right).

b) Calculate the volume of the shape.

3 cm
1 cm
2 cm
1 cm
1 cm
3 cm
2 cm
Side elevation

> Remember the formula —
> $V = L \times W \times H$

Time to test your skills with some more fancy shape constructions...

Q4 Use a ruler and a protractor to construct the following:

a) an equilateral triangle with sides 5 cm

b) a square with sides 6 cm

Q5 Construct these polygons:

a) a regular pentagon

b) a regular octagon

> Start these by drawing an accurate circle with a pair of compasses.

Transformations

Two whole pages of transformations for you here. And if that's not enough, you can find more on <u>pages 68 and 69</u>.

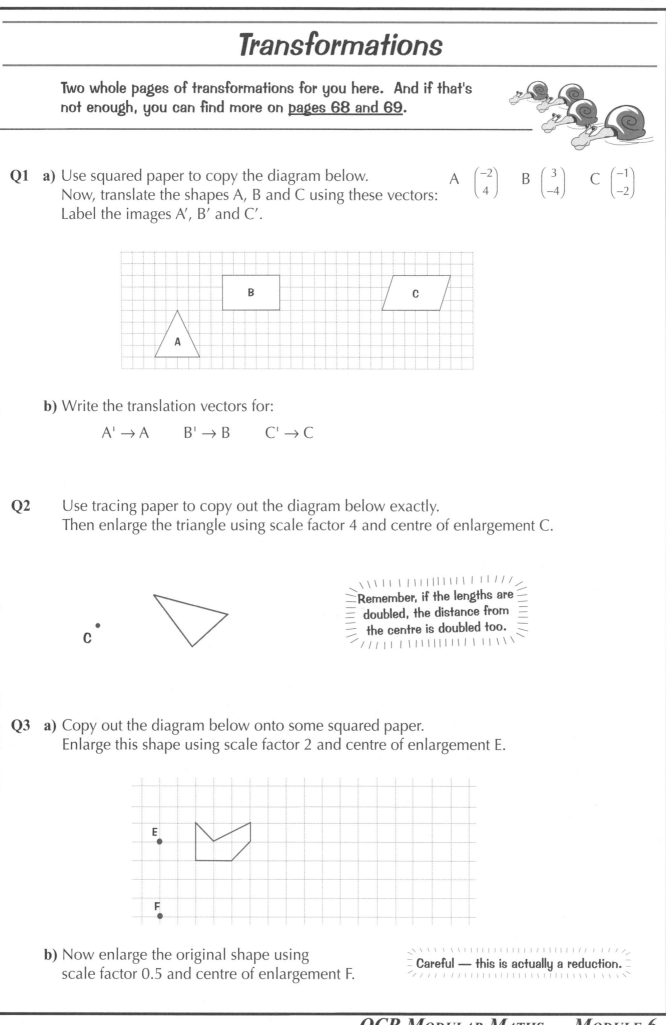

Q1 a) Use squared paper to copy the diagram below.
Now, translate the shapes A, B and C using these vectors:
Label the images A′, B′ and C′.

$$A \begin{pmatrix} -2 \\ 4 \end{pmatrix} \quad B \begin{pmatrix} 3 \\ -4 \end{pmatrix} \quad C \begin{pmatrix} -1 \\ -2 \end{pmatrix}$$

b) Write the translation vectors for:

$$A' \to A \qquad B' \to B \qquad C' \to C$$

Q2 Use tracing paper to copy out the diagram below exactly.
Then enlarge the triangle using scale factor 4 and centre of enlargement C.

Remember, if the lengths are doubled, the distance from the centre is doubled too.

Q3 a) Copy out the diagram below onto some squared paper.
Enlarge this shape using scale factor 2 and centre of enlargement E.

b) Now enlarge the original shape using scale factor 0.5 and centre of enlargement F.

Careful — this is actually a reduction.

Transformations

Q4 Use squared paper to copy the diagram below.
The centre of rotation for this diagram is O.

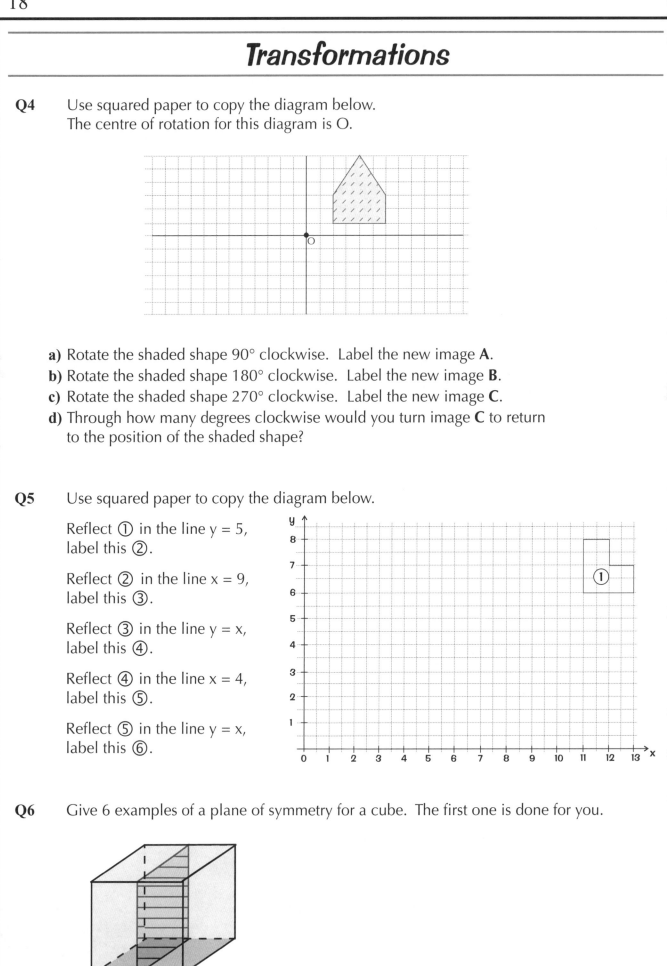

a) Rotate the shaded shape 90° clockwise. Label the new image **A**.

b) Rotate the shaded shape 180° clockwise. Label the new image **B**.

c) Rotate the shaded shape 270° clockwise. Label the new image **C**.

d) Through how many degrees clockwise would you turn image **C** to return to the position of the shaded shape?

Q5 Use squared paper to copy the diagram below.

Reflect ① in the line y = 5, label this ②.

Reflect ② in the line x = 9, label this ③.

Reflect ③ in the line y = x, label this ④.

Reflect ④ in the line x = 4, label this ⑤.

Reflect ⑤ in the line y = x, label this ⑥.

Q6 Give 6 examples of a plane of symmetry for a cube. The first one is done for you.

Probability

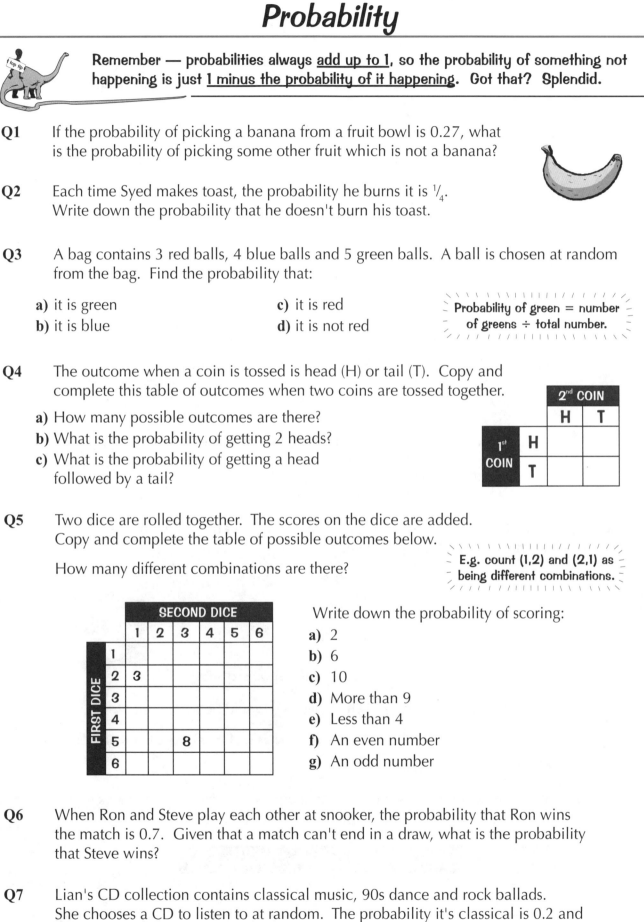

Remember — probabilities always <u>add up to 1</u>, so the probability of something not happening is just <u>1 minus the probability of it happening</u>. Got that? Splendid.

Q1 If the probability of picking a banana from a fruit bowl is 0.27, what is the probability of picking some other fruit which is not a banana?

Q2 Each time Syed makes toast, the probability he burns it is $\frac{1}{4}$.
Write down the probability that he doesn't burn his toast.

Q3 A bag contains 3 red balls, 4 blue balls and 5 green balls. A ball is chosen at random from the bag. Find the probability that:

a) it is green   **c)** it is red

b) it is blue   **d)** it is not red

Probability of green = number of greens ÷ total number.

Q4 The outcome when a coin is tossed is head (H) or tail (T). Copy and complete this table of outcomes when two coins are tossed together.

a) How many possible outcomes are there?
b) What is the probability of getting 2 heads?
c) What is the probability of getting a head followed by a tail?

		2nd COIN	
		H	**T**
1st COIN	**H**		
	T		

Q5 Two dice are rolled together. The scores on the dice are added.
Copy and complete the table of possible outcomes below.

How many different combinations are there?

E.g. count (1,2) and (2,1) as being different combinations.

		SECOND DICE					
		1	2	3	4	5	6
FIRST DICE	1						
	2	3					
	3						
	4						
	5		8				
	6						

Write down the probability of scoring:

a) 2
b) 6
c) 10
d) More than 9
e) Less than 4
f) An even number
g) An odd number

Q6 When Ron and Steve play each other at snooker, the probability that Ron wins the match is 0.7. Given that a match can't end in a draw, what is the probability that Steve wins?

Q7 Lian's CD collection contains classical music, 90s dance and rock ballads.
She chooses a CD to listen to at random. The probability it's classical is 0.2 and the probability it's 90s dance is 0.5.

Calculate the probability that she chooses rock ballads.

Averages

For module 6 you need to be able to calculate averages and range, and use them to compare sets of data. See page 80 for more questions on comparing data.

Q1 Here is a set of data: 5, 2, 3, 2, 9, 4, 2, 5

a) Calculate the mean for the data.
b) Calculate the median for the data.
c) Write down the mode for the data.
d) Work out the range of the data.

Put the data in order of size first — then it's easier to see which number you've got most of and to find the middle value.

Q2 Find the median, mode, mean and range of the following sets of data:

a) 20, 18, 16, 14, 12, 16, 0, 4, 6, 8
b) 5, 1, 2, 2, 4, 3, 3, 4, 3

Q3 The number of absences for 20 pupils during the spring term were:

0 0 0 0 0 0 1 1 1 2 3 4 4 4 7 9 10 10 19 22

a) Work out the mean, median and modal number of absences.

b) If you were a local newspaper reporter wishing to show that the local school has a very poor attendance record, which average would you use and why?

c) If you were the headteacher writing a report for the parents of new pupils, which average would you use and why?

Q4 The shoe sizes in a class of girls are:

3 3 4 4 5 5 5 5 6 6 6 7 8

a) Calculate the mean, median and mode for the shoe sizes.

b) If you were a shoe shop manager, which average would be most useful to you, and why?

Think about what each of the averages is actually telling you.

Q5 The National Tree Service has collected data on two woods. The diameters of young trees are calculated from their circumferences to the nearest centimetre.

diameter of trees	1 - 5	6 - 10	11 - 15	16 - 20	21 - 25	26 - 30	31 - 35	Total
Acornwood	1	5	8	20	4	1	1	40
Crookthwaite	6	4	5	4	7	3	1	30

Thin tree   Fat tree

Write down the modal class for the diameters of the trees in each wood.

Averages

Q6   These are some mathematics test marks for John and Mark.

John	65	83	58	79	75
Mark	72	70	81	67	70

a) Calculate the mean and range for each pupil.

b) Who do you think is the better maths student? Why?

Q7   The bar graph shows the amount of time Jim and Bob spend watching TV during the week.

a) Find the mean amount of time per day each spends watching TV.

b) Find the range of times for each of them.

c) Using your answers from **a)** and **b)**, comment on what you notice about the way they watch TV.

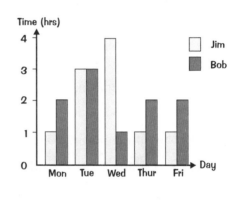

Q8   The Borders Orchid Growers Society has measured the heights of all the Lesser Plumed Bog Orchids in the 5 miles wide strip each side of the border, to the nearest cm.

5 miles on Scottish side
Heights 14, 15, 17, 14, 17, 16, 14, 13
15, 17, 16, 14, 15, 17, 14, 13

5 miles on English side
Heights 14, 12, 16, 18, 19, 17, 16, 15
13, 14, 15, 16, 17, 18, 19, 13

a) State the mode and median for each set of data.

b) Find the range for each set of data.

c) On which side of the border are you likely to see taller Orchids? Explain your answer.

d) On which side of the border are the orchids more of a standard size? Explain your answer.

Q9   The *Doughnut Standards Agency* has been called in to inspect two doughnut stalls.
They take samples of doughnuts and mark them out of 20. The marks are shown below.

Stall X	12	14	16	16	10	12	15	18	17	17
Stall Y	16	14	12	19	17	15	15	20	16	16

a) Calculate the mean and range for each of the samples.

b) Which doughnut stall would you recommend? Explain your answer.

Charts and Graphs

Q1 A baby was weighed every 5 days. The results are given in the table. Copy and complete the graph to show how the baby's weight changed.

DAY N°	0	5	10	15	20	25	30
WEIGHT KG	5.3	5.2	5.9	6.4	6.6	6.7	6.8

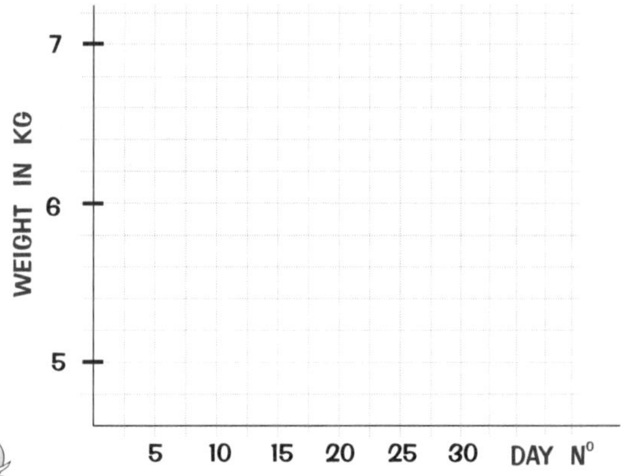

In your own words describe how the baby's weight changed:

Q2 This stem and leaf diagram shows the exam scores of a group of Year 9 pupils.

a) How many pupils got a score between 60 and 70?

b) How many scored 80 or more?

c) What was the most common test score?

d) Find the median score.

e) Calculate the range of scores.

```
3 | 2 3
4 | 6 8 8
5 | 1 2 2 3 6 6 9
6 | 1 5 5 5 8
7 | 2 3 4 5 8
8 | 0 1 1 5
9 | 0 2 3
```

Key: 5 | 2 means 52

Q3 I've been measuring my friends' noses. Here are the lengths in millimetres:

```
12   18   20   11   31
19   27   34   19   22
```

Copy and complete the stem and leaf diagram on the right to show these results.

```
1 |
2 |
3 |
```

Key: 2 | 3 means 23

Q4 **a)** Copy this stem and leaf diagram, and use the information from the line graph to complete it.

```
40 |
35 |
30 |
25 |
20 |
```

Key: 20 | 1 means 21

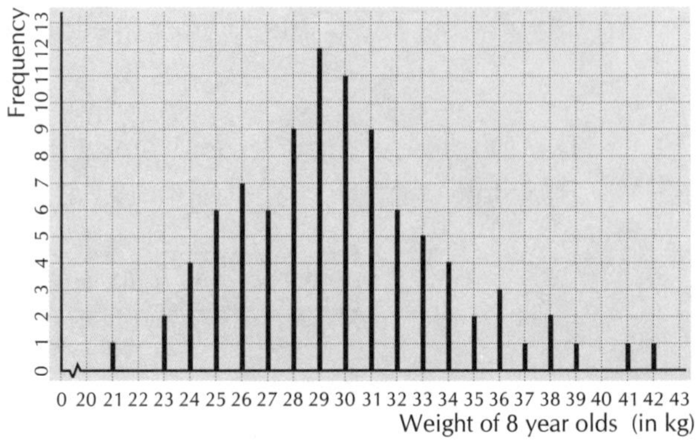

Weight of 8 year olds (in kg)

b) Write down the modal group.

Frequency Tables

Q1 Last season Newcaster City played 32 matches.
The number of goals they scored in each match were recorded as shown.

2	4	3	5		1	0	0	1
1	0	3	2		1	1	1	0
4	2	1	2		1	3	2	0
0	2	3	1		1	1	0	4

Fill in a copy of the tally chart. Copy and complete the frequency polygon of the goals.

GOALS	TALLY	FREQUENCY
0		
1		
2		
3		
4		
5		

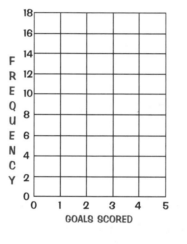

A <u>frequency polygon</u> is where you plot points for the frequencies and join them up with straight lines.

Q2 The frequency table below shows the number of hours spent Christmas shopping by 100 people surveyed in a town centre.

Number of Hours	0	1	2	3	4	5	6	7	8
Frequency	1	9	10	10	11	27	9	15	8
Hours × Frequency									

a) What is the modal number of hours spent Christmas shopping?

b) Fill in the third row of the table.

c) What is the total amount of time spent Christmas shopping by all the people surveyed?

d) What is the mean amount of time spent Christmas shopping by a person?

Scatter Graphs

Q1 These are the shoe sizes and heights for 12 pupils in Year 11.

Shoe size	5	6	4	6	7	7	8	3	5	9	10	10
Height (cm)	155	157	150	159	158	162	162	149	152	165	167	172

Copy the grid below and draw a scattergraph to show this information.

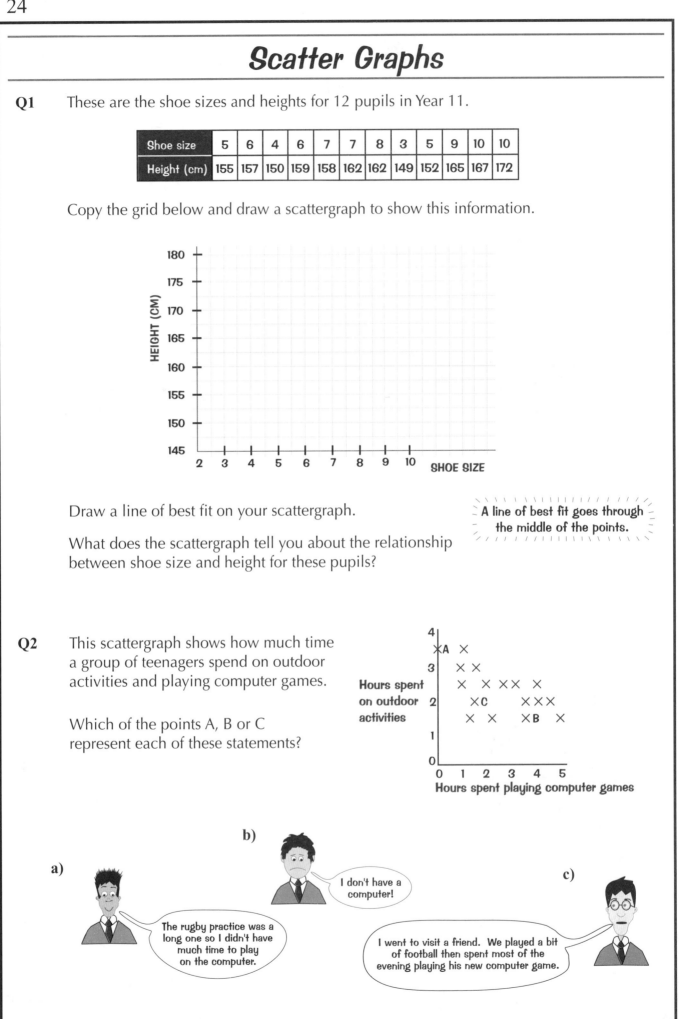

Draw a line of best fit on your scattergraph.

A line of best fit goes through the middle of the points.

What does the scattergraph tell you about the relationship between shoe size and height for these pupils?

Q2 This scattergraph shows how much time a group of teenagers spend on outdoor activities and playing computer games.

Which of the points A, B or C represent each of these statements?

b)

a) *The rugby practice was a long one so I didn't have much time to play on the computer.*

I don't have a computer!

c) *I went to visit a friend. We played a bit of football then spent most of the evening playing his new computer game.*

Powers

Now then, <u>**POWERS**</u> are just a way of writing numbers in shorthand — they come in handy with big numbers. Imagine writing out 2^{138} — $2 \times 2 \times ... \times 2 \times ... \times 2 \times$ yawn $\times$ zzz...

Q1 Copy and complete the following:

a) $2^4 = 2 \times 2 \times 2 \times 2 =$

b) $10^3 = 10 \times 10 \times 10 =$

c) $3^5 = 3 \times \qquad =$

d) $4^6 = 4 \times \qquad =$

e) $1^9 = 1 \times \qquad =$

f) $5^6 = 5 \times \qquad =$

Q2 Simplify the following:

a) $2 \times 2 \times 2 \times 2 \times 2 \times 2 \times 2 \times 2$

b) $12 \times 12 \times 12 \times 12 \times 12$

c) $m \times m \times m$

d) $y \times y \times y \times y$

Q3 Copy and complete the following (the first one has been done for you):

a) $10^2 \times 10^3 = \quad (10 \times 10) \times (10 \times 10 \times 10) \quad = 10^5$

b) $10^3 \times 10^4 = \qquad =$

c) $10^4 \times 10^2 = \qquad =$

d) What is the <u>quick method</u> for writing down the final result in **b)** and **c)**?

Q4 Copy and complete the following (the first one has been done for you):

a) $2^4 \div 2^2 = \dfrac{(2 \times 2 \times 2 \times 2)}{(2 \times 2)} = 2^2$

b) $2^5 \div 2^2 = \dfrac{(2 \times 2 \times 2 \times 2 \times 2)}{(2 \times 2)} =$

c) $4^5 \div 4^3 = \dfrac{(4 \times 4 \times 4 \times 4 \times 4)}{} =$

d) $8^5 \div 8^2 = \underline{\qquad\qquad} =$

e) What is the quick method for writing down the final result in **b)**, **c)** and **d)**?

Q5 Write the following as a <u>single term</u>:

a) $10^6 \div 10^4$

b) $(8^2 \times 8^5) \div 8^3$

c) $6^{10} \div (6^2 \times 6^3)$

d) $x^2 \times x^3$

e) $a^5 \times a^4$

f) $p^4 \times p^5 \times p^6$

Square Roots and Cube Roots

When you have "something ^{2} = a number", you find the "something" by taking the square root of the "number". But remember, you always get a + and – answer.

E.g. $x^2 = 49$ means that $x = \pm\sqrt{49} = +7$ or -7 (because $7 \times 7 = 49$ and $-7 \times -7 = 49$).

The " $\sqrt{}$ " sign means the positive square root.

Q1 Use the $\sqrt{}$ button on your calculator to find the following (positive) square roots to the nearest whole number.

a) $\sqrt{60}$
b) $\sqrt{19}$
c) $\sqrt{34}$
d) $\sqrt{200}$

e) $\sqrt{520}$
f) $\sqrt{75}$
g) $\sqrt{750}$
h) $\sqrt{0.9}$

i) $\sqrt{170}$
j) $\sqrt{7220}$
k) $\sqrt{1000050}$
l) $\sqrt{27}$

Q2 Without using a calculator, write down both answers to each of the following:

a) $x^2 = 4$
b) $x^2 = 16$
c) $x^2 = 9$
d) $x^2 = 49$

e) $x^2 = 25$
f) $x^2 = 100$
g) $x^2 = 144$
h) $x^2 = 64$

Q3 Use your calculator to find the following:

a) $\sqrt[3]{4096}$
b) $\sqrt[3]{1728}$
c) $\sqrt[3]{1331}$

d) $\sqrt[3]{1000000}$
e) $\sqrt[3]{1}$
f) $\sqrt[3]{0.125}$

Unlike square roots, cube roots only ever have one answer.

Q4 Without using a calculator, solve the following equations:

a) $x^3 = 64$
b) $x^3 = 512$
c) $x^3 = 125$

d) $x^3 = 1000$
e) $x^3 = 216$
f) $x^3 = 8000$

Q5 A square lawn has an area of 400 m^2.
What is the length of an edge?

Q6 A solid cube puzzle has a volume of 343 cm^3.
Find the length of one of its edges.

Checking and Estimating

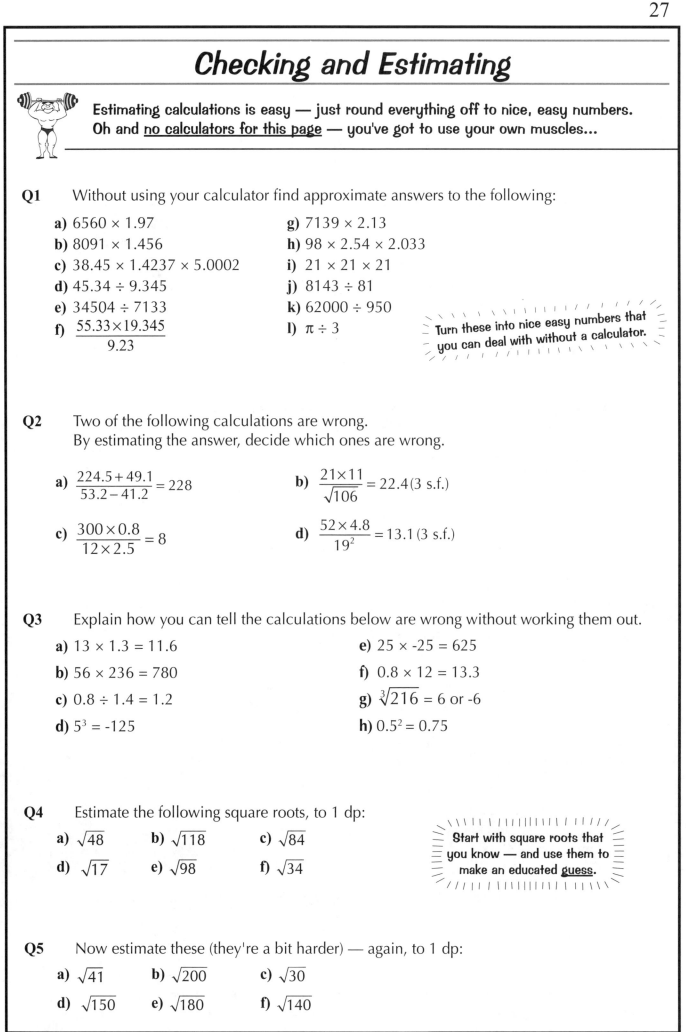

Estimating calculations is easy — just round everything off to nice, easy numbers. Oh and <u>no calculators for this page</u> — you've got to use your own muscles...

Q1 Without using your calculator find approximate answers to the following:

a) 6560×1.97
b) 8091×1.456
c) $38.45 \times 1.4237 \times 5.0002$
d) $45.34 \div 9.345$
e) $34504 \div 7133$
f) $\dfrac{55.33 \times 19.345}{9.23}$

g) 7139×2.13
h) $98 \times 2.54 \times 2.033$
i) $21 \times 21 \times 21$
j) $8143 \div 81$
k) $62000 \div 950$
l) $\pi \div 3$

Turn these into nice easy numbers that you can deal with without a calculator.

Q2 Two of the following calculations are wrong.
By estimating the answer, decide which ones are wrong.

a) $\dfrac{224.5 + 49.1}{53.2 - 41.2} = 228$

b) $\dfrac{21 \times 11}{\sqrt{106}} = 22.4\,(3\ \text{s.f.})$

c) $\dfrac{300 \times 0.8}{12 \times 2.5} = 8$

d) $\dfrac{52 \times 4.8}{19^2} = 13.1\,(3\ \text{s.f.})$

Q3 Explain how you can tell the calculations below are wrong without working them out.

a) $13 \times 1.3 = 11.6$
b) $56 \times 236 = 780$
c) $0.8 \div 1.4 = 1.2$
d) $5^3 = -125$

e) $25 \times \text{-}25 = 625$
f) $0.8 \times 12 = 13.3$
g) $\sqrt[3]{216} = 6 \text{ or } \text{-}6$
h) $0.5^2 = 0.75$

Q4 Estimate the following square roots, to 1 dp:

a) $\sqrt{48}$
b) $\sqrt{118}$
c) $\sqrt{84}$
d) $\sqrt{17}$
e) $\sqrt{98}$
f) $\sqrt{34}$

Start with square roots that you know — and use them to make an educated <u>guess</u>.

Q5 Now estimate these (they're a bit harder) — again, to 1 dp:

a) $\sqrt{41}$
b) $\sqrt{200}$
c) $\sqrt{30}$
d) $\sqrt{150}$
e) $\sqrt{180}$
f) $\sqrt{140}$

Ratio and Proportion

Q1   Write these ratios in their simplest forms:
  a) 6:8   **c)** 1.5:3   **e)** 2 weeks:4 days
  b) 5:20   **d)** 2¼:4   **f)** £1.26:14p

Q2   Concrete is mixed using cement, sand and gravel in the
       ratio 1:3:6. If a 5 kg bag of cement is used how much:
  a) sand is needed?
  b) gravel is needed?
       If the builder needs 80 kg of concrete,
  c) how much of each substance does he need?

Q3   Oak and ash saplings are planted along a roadside in the ratio 2:3 respectively.
       If there are 20 oak saplings, how many ash saplings are there?

Q4   A litre of Suzi's Strawberry Smoothy is to be divided between Dave, Dee and Daisy
       in the ratio 2:3:5. How many <u>millilitres</u> will each of them get?

Q5   Tony gives £100 to be shared by Jane, Paul and Rosemary in ratio according to their <u>age</u>.
       Jane is 10, Paul is 12 and Rosemary 3 years old. How much will each of them get?

> You can check your answer works to questions like this by adding
> up the individual amounts — they should add up to £100 here.

Q6   Now try these…

  a) Adam and Mags win £24 000. They split the money in the
       ratio 1 : 5. How much does Adam get?

  b) Sunil and Paul compete in a pizza eating contest. Between them they consume 28
       pizzas in the ratio 3 : 4. Who wins and how many did they eat?

  c) The total distance covered in a triathlon (swimming, cycling and running) is 15 km.
       It is split in the ratio 2 : 3 : 5. How far is each section?

Q7   At Sue's Tennis Star Hair salon, the amount that customers are charged is directly
       proportional to the time taken. As an example, Steffi paid £50 for a cut that took 1 hour.

  a) Andre has a head polish which takes 15 minutes. How much will this cost?

  b) Boris has a beard trim for 2.5 hours. How much will he have to pay?

  c) Bjorn has a "short Borg and sides" which costs £65. How long did it take?

If this well-proportioned page of ratio delights isn't enough for you,
there's plenty more ratio practice on <u>page 4</u> of module six.

Percentages

Q1 Express each of the following as a percentage. Round off if necessary.

a) £8 of £12

b) £7 of £16

c) 600 kg of 750 kg

d) 6 hours of one day

e) 1 month of a year

f) 25 m of 65 m

Q2 Admission to Wonder World is <u>£18 for adults</u>. A child ticket is <u>60%</u> of the adult price.

a) How much will it cost for one adult and four children to enter Wonder World?

b) How much will two adults and three children spend on entrance tickets?

Q3 Terence paid £4700 for his new motorcycle. <u>Each year</u> its value decreased by 12%.

a) How much was it worth when it was one year old?

b) How much was it worth when it was two years old?

Q4 Ed is thinking of buying either a silly sports car for £3000 or a sensible people-carrier for £3700. The value of the people-carrier will depreciate by 30% each year. The sports car will hold its value better, depreciating by 20% each year.

a) How much will each car be worth in 1 year?

b) Which car will be worth more in 2 years time?

Q5 a) A 5kg pumpkin increases in weight by 60% over a fortnight. Find its new weight.

b) A 15 cm tall leek increases in height by 30%. Find its new height.

c) A freshly picked radish weighs 20 g. A week later it has shrivelled up and decreased in weight by 40%. Find its new weight.

d) Tom gets 15% lighter after eating only pumpkins, leeks and radishes for a month. If he weighed 80 kg to start with how much will he weigh now?

Q6 a) Mani books a jungle-trekking holiday to Peru. The price is £1500 plus a 5% fee to cover insurance and booking costs. How much will Mani have to pay?

b) Sam books a jungle-trekking holiday to Blackpool. The normal cost is £59, but it currently has a 35% discount. How much will Sam have to pay?

With a bit of <u>cunning</u>, percentage increase and decrease problems can be solved with just a single multiplication. It's all a question of picking the <u>right multiplier</u>:

E.g. if a 10 kg cat gets 25% heavier, it will be 10 × 1.25 = 12.5 kg.
if a 10 kg cat gets 25% lighter, it will be 10 × 0.75 = 7.5 kg.

Multiples and Factors

The multiples of a number are its times table — if you need multiples of more than one number, do them separately then pick the ones in both lists.

Q1 What are the first five multiples of:

    a) 4?

    b) 7?

    c) 12?

    d) 18?

Q2 Find a number which is a multiple of:

    a) 2 and 6

    b) 7 and 5

    c) 2 and 3 and 7

    d) 4 and 5 and 9

Factors multiply together to make other numbers.
E.g. $\underline{1 \times 6 = 6}$ and $\underline{2 \times 3 = 6}$, so $\underline{\text{6 has factors 1, 2, 3 and 6}}$.

Q3 **a)** I am a factor of 24.
I am an odd number.
I am bigger than 1.
What number am I?

    b) I am a factor of 30.
I am an even number.
I am less than 5.
What number am I?

Q4 A perfect number is one where the factors add up to the number itself.
For example, the factors of 28 are 1, 2, 4, 7 and 14 (not including 28 itself).
These add up to $1 + 2 + 4 + 7 + 14 = 28$, and so 28 is a perfect number.

Complete this table, and circle the perfect number in the left hand column.

Number	Factors (excluding the number itself)	Sum of Factors
2		
4	1, 2	3
6		
8		
10		

The sum of the factors is all the factors added together.

Q5 **a)** What is the biggest number that is a factor of both 42 and 18?

    b) What is the smallest number that has both 4 and 18 as factors?

Prime Numbers

Basically, prime numbers don't divide by anything (except 1 and themselves).
5 is prime — it will only divide by 1 or 5. 1 is an exception to this rule — it is not prime.

Q1   Write down the first ten prime numbers.

Q2   Give a reason for 27 not being a prime number.

Q3   Using any or all of the figures **1, 2, 3, 7** write down:

    a) the smallest prime number

    b) a prime number greater than 20

    c) a prime number between 10 and 20

    d) two prime numbers whose sum is 20

    e) a number that is not prime.

Q4   Find all the prime numbers between 40 and 50.

Q5   In a copy of the <u>ten by ten square</u>
opposite, ring all the prime numbers.

    The first three have been done for you.

1	②	③	4	⑤	6	7	8	9	10
11	12	13	14	15	16	17	18	19	20
21	22	23	24	25	26	27	28	29	30
31	32	33	34	35	36	37	38	39	40
41	42	43	44	45	46	47	48	49	50
51	52	53	54	55	56	57	58	59	60
61	62	63	64	65	66	67	68	69	70
71	72	73	74	75	76	77	78	79	80
81	82	83	84	85	86	87	88	89	90
91	92	93	94	95	96	97	98	99	100

Q6   A school ran three evening classes: <u>judo, karate and kendo</u>.
The judo class had 29 pupils, the karate class had 27 and the kendo class 23.
For which classes would the teacher have difficulty dividing the pupils into equal groups?

Q7   Find three sets of three prime numbers which add up to the following numbers:

10   **29**   **41**

HCF, LCM and Prime Factors

Q1 For each set of numbers find the HCF.

a) 40, 60   d) 15, 45   g) 32, 64

b) 10, 40, 60   e) 15, 30, 45   h) 32, 48, 64

c) 10, 24, 40, 60   f) 15, 20, 30, 45   i) 16, 32, 48, 64

Q2 For each set of numbers find the LCM.

a) 40, 60   d) 15, 45   g) 32, 64

b) 10, 40, 60   e) 15, 30, 45   h) 32, 48, 64

c) 10, 24, 40, 60   f) 15, 20, 30, 45   i) 16, 32, 48, 64

Q3 Lars, Rita and Alan regularly go swimming. Lars goes every 2 days, Rita goes every 3 days and Alan goes every 5 days. They <u>all</u> went swimming together on Friday 1st June.

a) On what <u>date</u> will Lars and Rita next go swimming together?

b) On what <u>date</u> will Rita and Alan next go swimming together?

c) On what <u>day of the week</u> will all 3 next go swimming together?

This is a LCM question in disguise.

d) Which of the 3 (if any) will go swimming on 15th June?

Q4 Complete the factor trees below to express each number as a product of prime factors. The first one has been done for you.

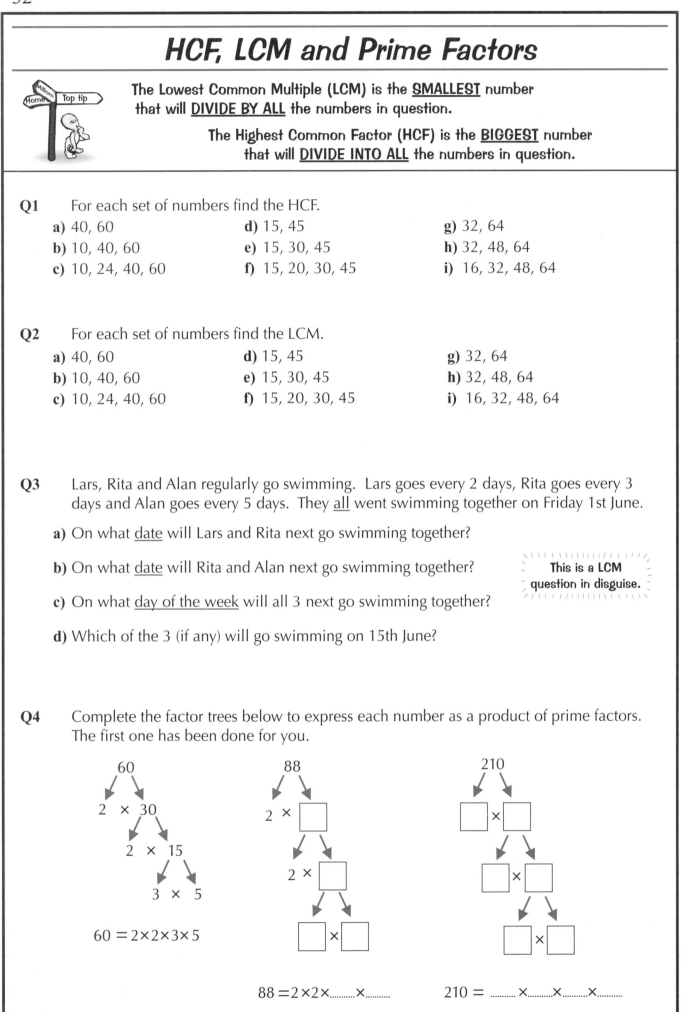

$$60 = 2 \times 2 \times 3 \times 5$$

$$88 = 2 \times 2 \times \text{......} \times \text{......}$$

$$210 = \text{......} \times \text{......} \times \text{......} \times \text{......}$$

Number Sequences

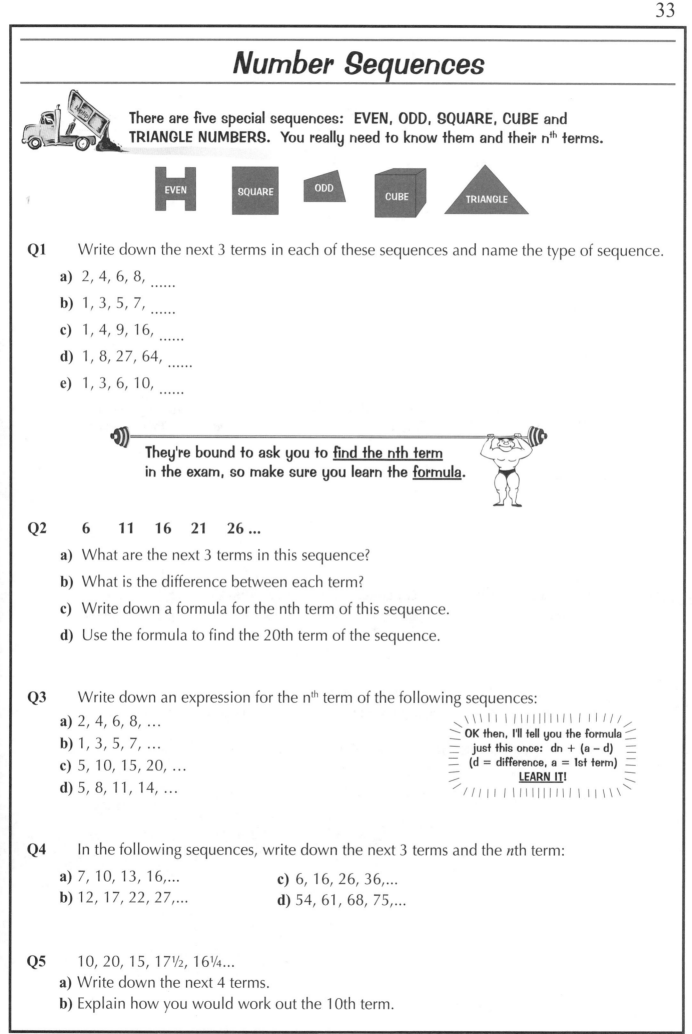

There are five special sequences: EVEN, ODD, SQUARE, CUBE and TRIANGLE NUMBERS. You really need to know them and their n^{th} terms.

Q1 Write down the next 3 terms in each of these sequences and name the type of sequence.

a) 2, 4, 6, 8, ...

b) 1, 3, 5, 7, ...

c) 1, 4, 9, 16, ...

d) 1, 8, 27, 64, ...

e) 1, 3, 6, 10, ...

They're bound to ask you to <u>find the nth term</u> in the exam, so make sure you learn the <u>formula</u>.

Q2 6   11   16   21   26 ...

a) What are the next 3 terms in this sequence?

b) What is the difference between each term?

c) Write down a formula for the nth term of this sequence.

d) Use the formula to find the 20th term of the sequence.

Q3 Write down an expression for the nth term of the following sequences:

a) 2, 4, 6, 8, ...

b) 1, 3, 5, 7, ...

c) 5, 10, 15, 20, ...

d) 5, 8, 11, 14, ...

OK then, I'll tell you the formula just this once: dn + (a – d)
(d = difference, a = 1st term)
<u>LEARN IT!</u>

Q4 In the following sequences, write down the next 3 terms and the *n*th term:

a) 7, 10, 13, 16,...

b) 12, 17, 22, 27,...

c) 6, 16, 26, 36,...

d) 54, 61, 68, 75,...

Q5 10, 20, 15, 17½, 16¼...

a) Write down the next 4 terms.

b) Explain how you would work out the 10th term.

Equations and Formulas

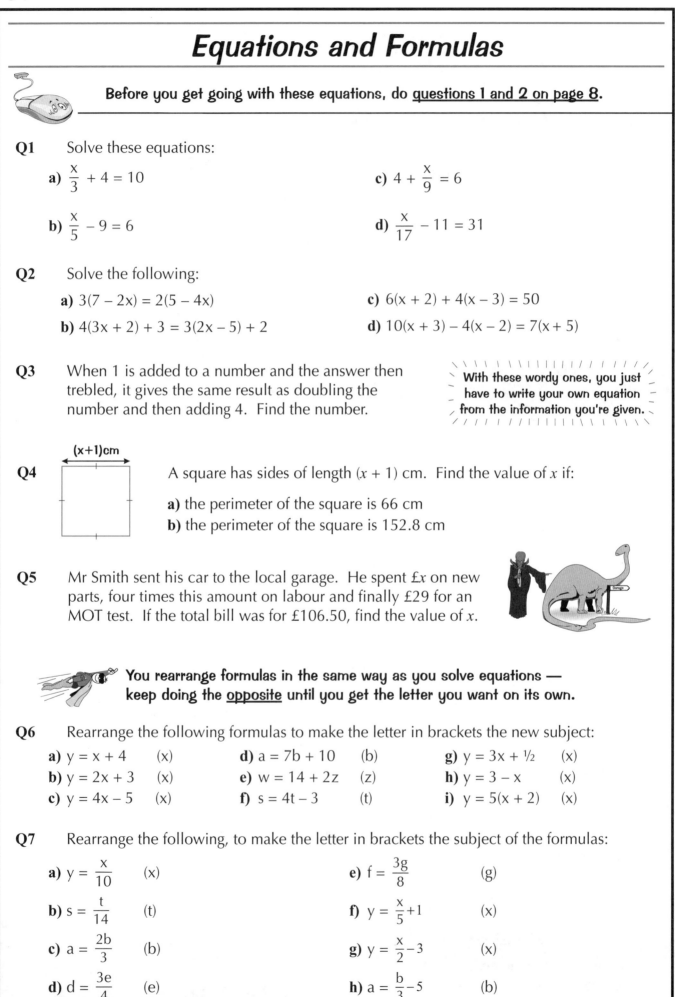

Before you get going with these equations, do <u>questions 1 and 2 on page 8</u>.

Q1 Solve these equations:

a) $\frac{x}{3} + 4 = 10$

c) $4 + \frac{x}{9} = 6$

b) $\frac{x}{5} - 9 = 6$

d) $\frac{x}{17} - 11 = 31$

Q2 Solve the following:

a) $3(7 - 2x) = 2(5 - 4x)$

c) $6(x + 2) + 4(x - 3) = 50$

b) $4(3x + 2) + 3 = 3(2x - 5) + 2$

d) $10(x + 3) - 4(x - 2) = 7(x + 5)$

Q3 When 1 is added to a number and the answer then trebled, it gives the same result as doubling the number and then adding 4. Find the number.

With these wordy ones, you just have to write your own equation from the information you're given.

(x+1)cm

Q4 A square has sides of length $(x + 1)$ cm. Find the value of x if:

a) the perimeter of the square is 66 cm

b) the perimeter of the square is 152.8 cm

Q5 Mr Smith sent his car to the local garage. He spent £x on new parts, four times this amount on labour and finally £29 for an MOT test. If the total bill was for £106.50, find the value of x.

You rearrange formulas in the same way as you solve equations — keep doing the <u>opposite</u> until you get the letter you want on its own.

Q6 Rearrange the following formulas to make the letter in brackets the new subject:

a) $y = x + 4$ (x)

d) $a = 7b + 10$ (b)

g) $y = 3x + \frac{1}{2}$ (x)

b) $y = 2x + 3$ (x)

e) $w = 14 + 2z$ (z)

h) $y = 3 - x$ (x)

c) $y = 4x - 5$ (x)

f) $s = 4t - 3$ (t)

i) $y = 5(x + 2)$ (x)

Q7 Rearrange the following, to make the letter in brackets the subject of the formulas:

a) $y = \frac{x}{10}$ (x)

e) $f = \frac{3g}{8}$ (g)

b) $s = \frac{t}{14}$ (t)

f) $y = \frac{x}{5} + 1$ (x)

c) $a = \frac{2b}{3}$ (b)

g) $y = \frac{x}{2} - 3$ (x)

d) $d = \frac{3e}{4}$ (e)

h) $a = \frac{b}{3} - 5$ (b)

Equations and Formulas

Q8 The total number of CDs owned by two friends is given by:
Number of CDs owned by Chloe, x, + number of CDs owned by Sadiki, w.
Write down a formula for the total number, N, of CDs they own.

Q9 Write a formula for:

a) The perimeter, P, of a square which is equal
to the side length, d, multiplied by 4.
b) The area, A, of a square which is equal to the length, d, multiplied by the width, d.

Q10 a) To find y, multiply x by 4 and then subtract 2. Write a formula for y.

b) To find y, square x, add 2x and subtract 6. Write a formula for y.

Q11 Tickets for a football match cost £x each. Write a formula for the cost in pounds, C, of:

a) 2 tickets
b) n tickets

CGP Wanderers Football Club
Vs United Rovers FC
Comfy Seat
East stand lower bit
Row 20
Seat 104
£25.00

Q12 Feeding the toucans at the zoo costs 20p, plus 50p for every bag of food you buy.
Write a formula for the total cost in pence, C, of feeding the toucans with n bags of food.

Q13 Calculate the value of R from the formula $R = s^2 + 5t$ when:
a) s = 2, t = -3 **b)** s = -2, t = 3

Q14 The time taken to cook a chicken is given as 20
minutes per lb plus 20 minutes extra. Find the time
needed to cook a chicken weighing:

a) 4 lb **b)** 7.5 lb

Q15 This rectangle has length l cm and width w cm. Its perimeter is p cm.

a) Write down a formula with p as the subject.
b) Find the perimeter of the rectangle when l = 12 and w = 5.
c) Rearrange your formula from part **a)** to make l the subject.

Q16 A car sales person is paid £w for working m months and selling c cars,
where w = 500m + 50c.

a) Rearrange the formula to make c the subject.
b) Find the number of cars the sales person sells in 11 months if he earns £12,100
during that time.

**Want more formula questions? You're in luck. Take a peek back at
page 8 if you want to practise some more substituting into formulas.**

Algebra

The best way to multiply two brackets together is to use the <u>FOIL</u> method — <u>F</u>irsts, <u>O</u>utsides, <u>I</u>nsides, <u>L</u>asts.

Q1 For each of the large rectangles below, write down the area of the four smaller rectangles.

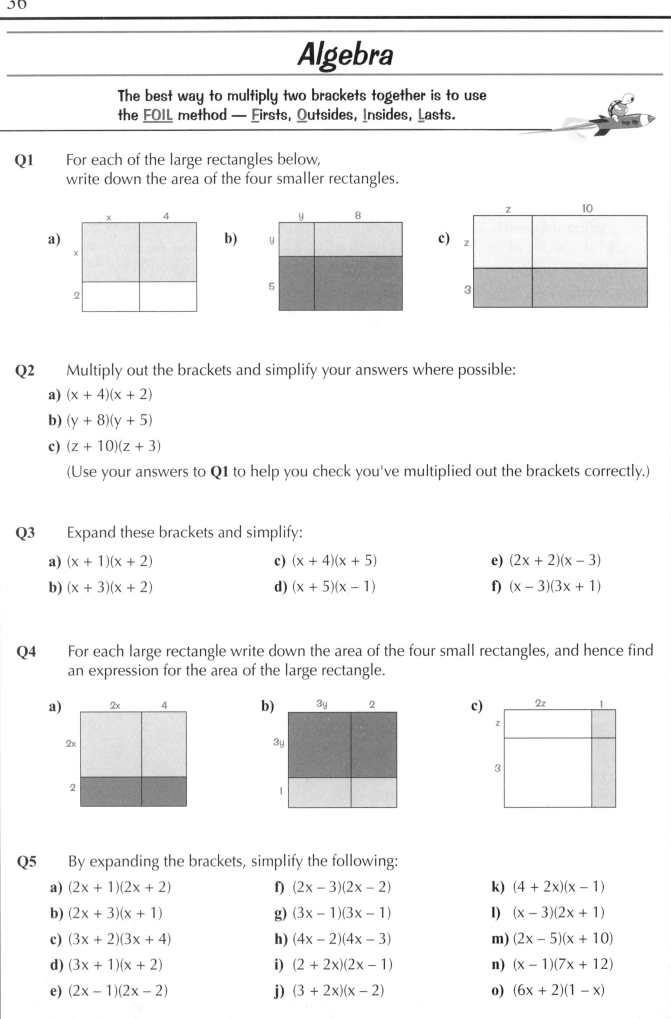

a)

b)

c)

Q2 Multiply out the brackets and simplify your answers where possible:

a) $(x + 4)(x + 2)$

b) $(y + 8)(y + 5)$

c) $(z + 10)(z + 3)$

(Use your answers to **Q1** to help you check you've multiplied out the brackets correctly.)

Q3 Expand these brackets and simplify:

a) $(x + 1)(x + 2)$ **c)** $(x + 4)(x + 5)$ **e)** $(2x + 2)(x − 3)$

b) $(x + 3)(x + 2)$ **d)** $(x + 5)(x − 1)$ **f)** $(x − 3)(3x + 1)$

Q4 For each large rectangle write down the area of the four small rectangles, and hence find an expression for the area of the large rectangle.

a)

b)

c)

Q5 By expanding the brackets, simplify the following:

a) $(2x + 1)(2x + 2)$ **f)** $(2x − 3)(2x − 2)$ **k)** $(4 + 2x)(x − 1)$

b) $(2x + 3)(x + 1)$ **g)** $(3x − 1)(3x − 1)$ **l)** $(x − 3)(2x + 1)$

c) $(3x + 2)(3x + 4)$ **h)** $(4x − 2)(4x − 3)$ **m)** $(2x − 5)(x + 10)$

d) $(3x + 1)(x + 2)$ **i)** $(2 + 2x)(2x − 1)$ **n)** $(x − 1)(7x + 12)$

e) $(2x − 1)(2x − 2)$ **j)** $(3 + 2x)(x − 2)$ **o)** $(6x + 2)(1 − x)$

Inequalities

Yet another one of those bits of Maths that looks worse than it is —
these are just like equations, really, except for the symbols.

Q1 Write down an inequality for each of the diagrams below.

a)

b)

c)

d)

e)

f)

g)

h)

i)

j)

k)

l)

Q2 By drawing an appropriate part of the number line, show the part of the number line described by each of the following inequalities.

a) $x \geqslant 3$

b) $x < -1$

c) $x > 5$

d) $x \leqslant 2$

e) $2 > x > -5$

f) $3 > x \geqslant -2$

g) $-2 \leqslant x \leqslant 0$

h) $-4 < x \leqslant 1$

i) $3 \geqslant x > -2$

j) $7 \geqslant x > 6$

k) $-3 \leqslant x \leqslant -2$

l) $0 \geqslant x > -3$

Q3 Solve the following inequalities:

a) $2x \geqslant 16$

b) $4x > -20$

c) $x + 2 > 5$

d) $x - 3 \leqslant 10$

e) $x + 4 \geqslant 14$

f) $10x > -2$

g) $5 + x \geqslant 12$

h) $x/4 > 10$

i) $x/3 \leqslant 1$

j) $x/2 \leqslant 4$

k) $5x + 4 < 24$

l) $5x + 7 \leqslant 32$

m) $3x + 12 \leqslant 30$

n) $2x - 7 \geqslant 8$

o) $17 + 4x < 33$

Q4 There are 1,130 pupils in a school and no classes have more than 32 pupils. What is the least number of classrooms that could be used? Show this information as an inequality.

Call the number of classrooms x.

Quadratic Graphs

If an expression has an x^2 term as the <u>highest power</u>, it's quadratic. The graphs you get from quadratic expressions are always curves with a certain shape.

Q1   Copy and complete this table of values for the quadratic graph $y = 2x^2$.

a) On graph paper, draw axes with x from -4 to 4 and y from 0 to 32.

x	-4	-3	-2	-1	0	1	2	3	4
$y=2x^2$	32	18					8		

Remember to square first then x 2

b) Plot the 9 points and join them with a smooth curve.

Q2   Copy and complete this table of values for the graph $y = x^2 + x$.

x	-4	-3	-2	-1	0	1	2	3	4
x^2	16	9					4		
$y=x^2+x$	12					2			

By putting more steps in your table of values, the arithmetic is easier

a) On graph paper, draw axes with x from -4 to 4 and y from 0 to 20.

b) Plot the points and join them with a smooth curve.

c) Use your graph to find the two solutions of the equation $x^2 + x = 0$.

Just find the x-values where the graph crosses the x-axis (i.e. where y = 0).

Q3 a) Copy and complete this table of values for the graph $y = x^2 - 4x + 1$.

x	-2	-1	0	1	2	3	4
x^2	4	1				9	
-4x	8					-12	
1	1	1				1	
$y=x^2-4x+1$	13	6				-2	

b) Plot the graph $y = x^2 - 4x + 1$, using axes with x from -2 to 4 and y from -3 to 13.

c) Use your graph to find approximate solutions of the equation $x^2 - 4x + 1 = 0$.

Quadratic Graphs

Q4 Copy and complete this table for $y = x^2 - 4$:

x	-4	-3	-2	-1	0	1	2	3	4
x^2									
-4									
y									

Draw the graph $y = x^2 - 4$
Use your graph to solve the following equations (to 1 d.p.):

a) $x^2 - 4 = 1$

b) $x^2 - 4 = 0$

You're looking for the values of x
which correspond to $y = 1$ and 0.

 If the x^2 term has a <u>minus</u> sign in front of it, the bucket will be turned <u>upside down</u>.

Q5 a) Copy and complete this table of values for the graph $y = 3 - x^2$.

x	-4	-3	-2	-1	0	1	2	3	4
3	3	3	3	3	3	3	3	3	3
$-x^2$	-16						-4		
$y=3-x^2$	-13						-1		

b) Draw the graph $y = 3 - x^2$ for x from -4 to 4.

c) Use your graph to find approximate solutions of the equation $3 - x^2 = 0$.

Q6 a) Draw the graph $y = -x^2 + x + 4$ for values of x from -3 to 4.

b) Use your graph to find approximate solutions to the equation $-x^2 + x + 4 = 0$.

If any points look a bit strange, check you've got them right in the <u>table of values</u>.
I know it's boring doing it all again, but it shouldn't be too hard if you've put all
the steps in. **And** it'll mean you <u>don't get it wrong</u>. Which is always nice.

Trial and Improvement

Q1 Use the trial and improvement method to solve the equation $x^3 = 50$.
Give your answer to 1 d.p. Two trials have been done for you.

Try $x = 3$, $x^3 = 27$ (too small)
Try $x = 4$, $x^3 = 64$ (too big)

Ooh look — opposite cases. So the
solution must be between 3 and 4.

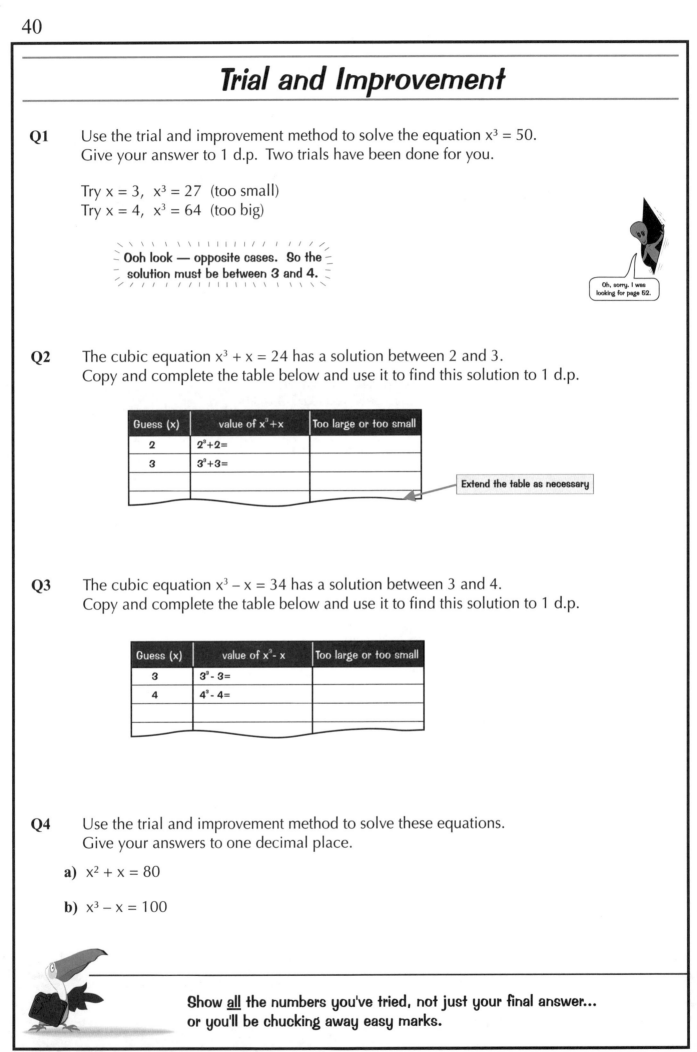

Oh, sorry. I was
looking for page 52.

Q2 The cubic equation $x^3 + x = 24$ has a solution between 2 and 3.
Copy and complete the table below and use it to find this solution to 1 d.p.

Guess (x)	value of $x^3 + x$	Too large or too small
2	$2^3 + 2 =$	
3	$3^3 + 3 =$	

Extend the table as necessary

Q3 The cubic equation $x^3 - x = 34$ has a solution between 3 and 4.
Copy and complete the table below and use it to find this solution to 1 d.p.

Guess (x)	value of $x^3 - x$	Too large or too small
3	$3^3 - 3 =$	
4	$4^3 - 4 =$	

Q4 Use the trial and improvement method to solve these equations.
Give your answers to one decimal place.

a) $x^2 + x = 80$

b) $x^3 - x = 100$

Show **all** the numbers you've tried, not just your final answer...
or you'll be chucking away easy marks.

Circles — Geometry Problems

Remember these 2 rules for circle geometry problems:

1) **ANGLE FORMED IN A SEMI-CIRCLE = 90°**

2) **ANGLE BETWEEN TANGENT AND RADIUS = 90°**

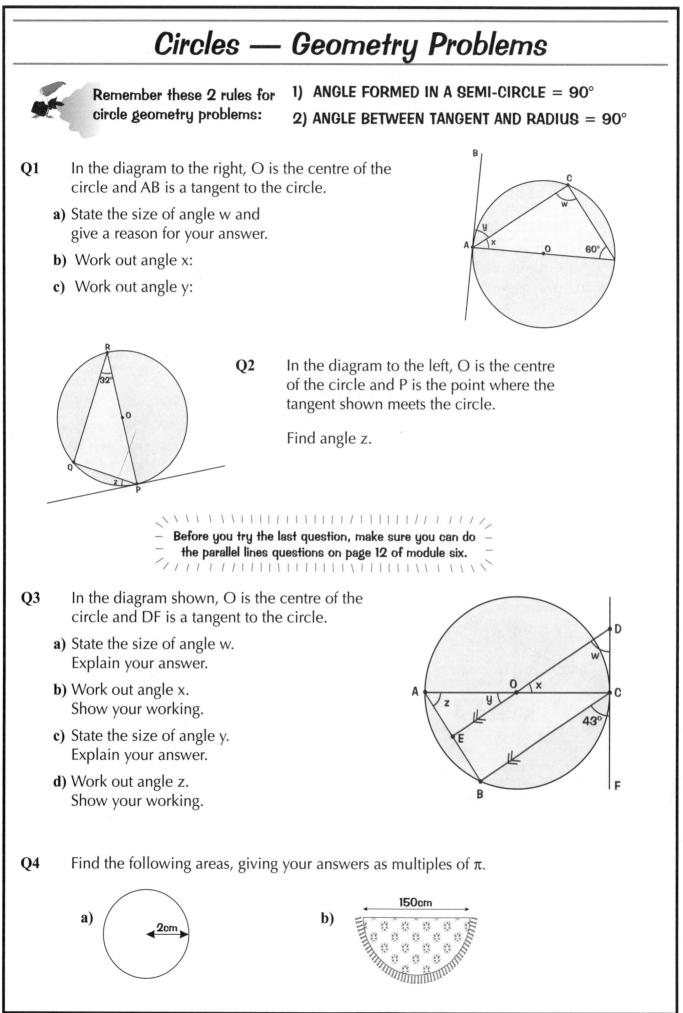

Q1 In the diagram to the right, O is the centre of the circle and AB is a tangent to the circle.

a) State the size of angle w and give a reason for your answer.

b) Work out angle x:

c) Work out angle y:

Q2 In the diagram to the left, O is the centre of the circle and P is the point where the tangent shown meets the circle.

Find angle z.

＼＼＼＼＼＼＼＼＼｜｜｜｜｜｜｜｜｜｜｜｜｜｜｜／｜｜｜｜｜｜／／／／／／／／
Before you try the last question, make sure you can do the parallel lines questions on page 12 of module six.
／／／／／／／／｜｜｜｜｜｜｜｜｜｜｜｜｜＼｜｜｜｜｜｜＼＼＼＼＼

Q3 In the diagram shown, O is the centre of the circle and DF is a tangent to the circle.

a) State the size of angle w. Explain your answer.

b) Work out angle x. Show your working.

c) State the size of angle y. Explain your answer.

d) Work out angle z. Show your working.

Q4 Find the following areas, giving your answers as multiples of π.

a)

b)

150cm

Pythagoras' Theorem

Pythagoras' formula is an awkward little sausage. My advice is to learn this foolproof method for using it, then it shouldn't cause you any headaches:

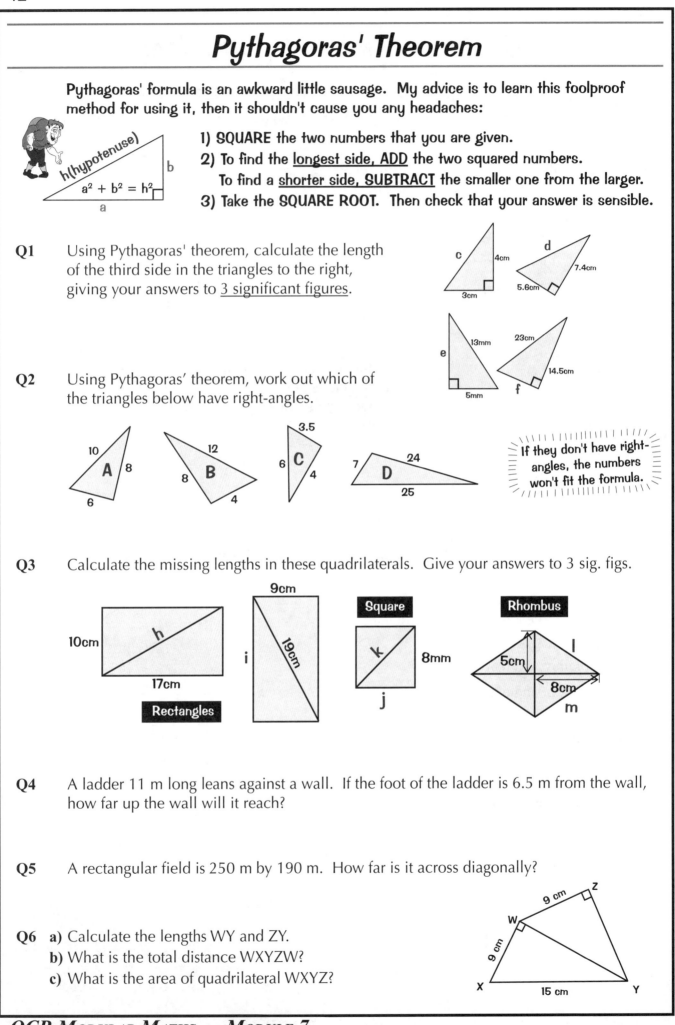

1) **SQUARE** the two numbers that you are given.
2) To find the <u>longest side, **ADD**</u> the two squared numbers.
   To find a <u>shorter side, **SUBTRACT**</u> the smaller one from the larger.
3) Take the **SQUARE ROOT**. Then check that your answer is sensible.

Q1 Using Pythagoras' theorem, calculate the length of the third side in the triangles to the right, giving your answers to <u>3 significant figures</u>.

Q2 Using Pythagoras' theorem, work out which of the triangles below have right-angles.

> If they don't have right-angles, the numbers won't fit the formula.

Q3 Calculate the missing lengths in these quadrilaterals. Give your answers to 3 sig. figs.

Q4 A ladder 11 m long leans against a wall. If the foot of the ladder is 6.5 m from the wall, how far up the wall will it reach?

Q5 A rectangular field is 250 m by 190 m. How far is it across diagonally?

Q6 a) Calculate the lengths WY and ZY.
   b) What is the total distance WXYZW?
   c) What is the area of quadrilateral WXYZ?

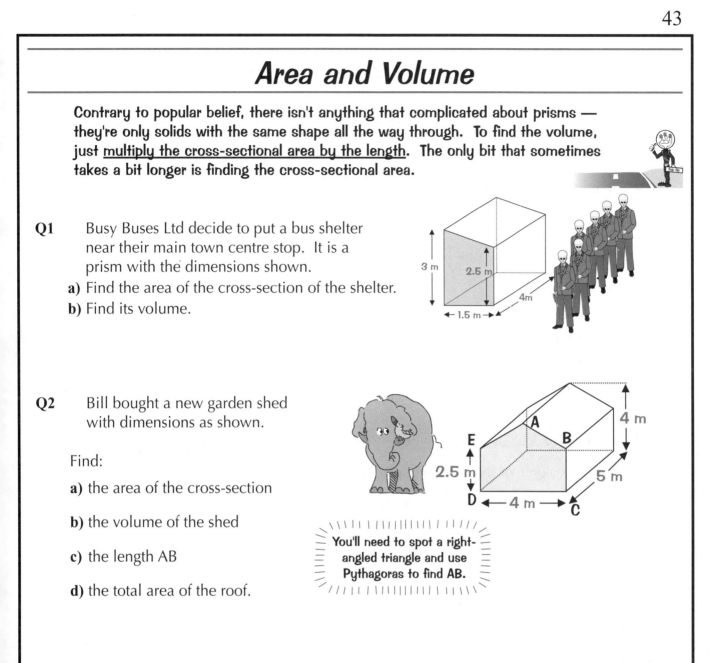

Area and Volume

Contrary to popular belief, there isn't anything that complicated about prisms — they're only solids with the same shape all the way through. To find the volume, just <u>multiply the cross-sectional area by the length</u>. The only bit that sometimes takes a bit longer is finding the cross-sectional area.

Q1 Busy Buses Ltd decide to put a bus shelter near their main town centre stop. It is a prism with the dimensions shown.
a) Find the area of the cross-section of the shelter.
b) Find its volume.

Q2 Bill bought a new garden shed with dimensions as shown.

Find:

a) the area of the cross-section

b) the volume of the shed

c) the length AB

d) the total area of the roof.

You'll need to spot a right-angled triangle and use Pythagoras to find AB.

Q3 Rubber chocks are put under the wheels of aeroplanes to stop them moving when on the ground. A typical chock is shown.

a) Calculate the volume of the chock.

b) Calculate its surface area.

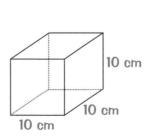

The surface area is made up of 2 identical trapesiums + 4 different rectangles.

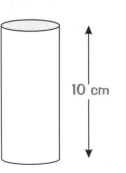

Q4 A solid metal cube, each of whose sides is 10 cm long, is melted down and made into a solid cylinder 10 cm high.

a) What is the radius of this cylinder?

b) Find the surface area of the cylinder.

Area and Volume

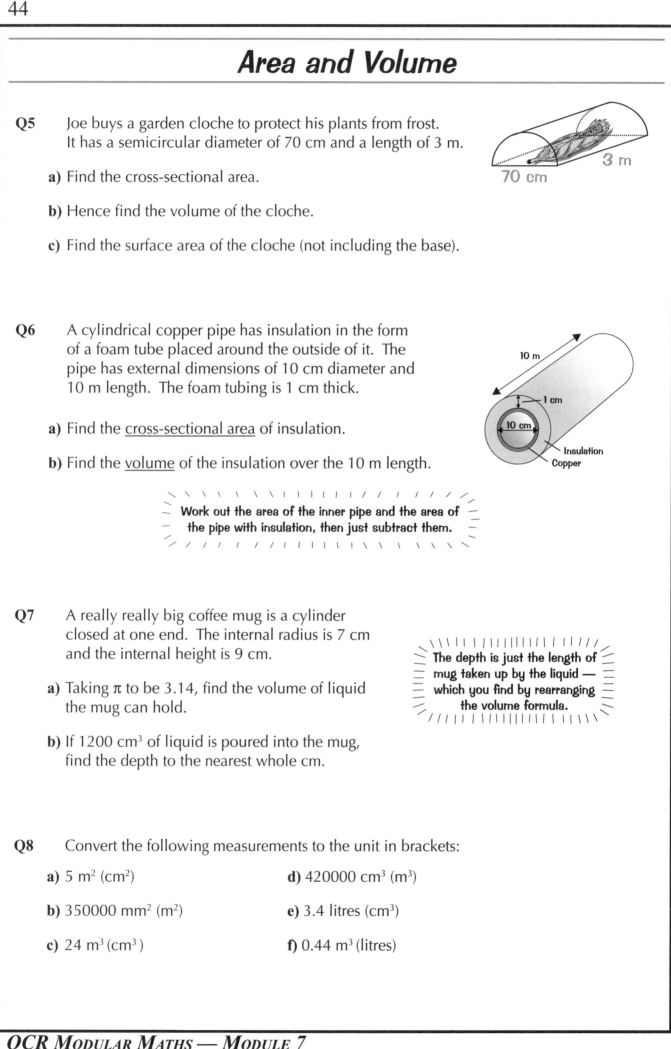

Q5 Joe buys a garden cloche to protect his plants from frost.
It has a semicircular diameter of 70 cm and a length of 3 m.

a) Find the cross-sectional area.

b) Hence find the volume of the cloche.

c) Find the surface area of the cloche (not including the base).

70 cm   3 m

Q6 A cylindrical copper pipe has insulation in the form
of a foam tube placed around the outside of it. The
pipe has external dimensions of 10 cm diameter and
10 m length. The foam tubing is 1 cm thick.

a) Find the <u>cross-sectional area</u> of insulation.

b) Find the <u>volume</u> of the insulation over the 10 m length.

10 m
1 cm
10 cm
Insulation
Copper

> Work out the area of the inner pipe and the area of
> the pipe with insulation, then just subtract them.

Q7 A really really big coffee mug is a cylinder
closed at one end. The internal radius is 7 cm
and the internal height is 9 cm.

a) Taking π to be 3.14, find the volume of liquid
the mug can hold.

b) If 1200 cm³ of liquid is poured into the mug,
find the depth to the nearest whole cm.

> The depth is just the length of
> mug taken up by the liquid —
> which you find by rearranging
> the volume formula.

Q8 Convert the following measurements to the unit in brackets:

a) 5 m² (cm²)

b) 350000 mm² (m²)

c) 24 m³ (cm³)

d) 420000 cm³ (m³)

e) 3.4 litres (cm³)

f) 0.44 m³ (litres)

Coordinates

Q1 Find the midpoint of the line segments AB, where A and B have coordinates:

a) A(2,3) B(4,5)

b) A(1,8) B(9,2)

c) A(0,11) B(12,11)

d) A(3,15) B(13,3)

e) A(6,6) B(0,0)

f) A(15,9) B(3,3)

Your answers should be coordinates too.

Q2 Find the midpoints of each of these line segments:

a) Line segment PQ, where P has coordinates (1,5) and Q has coordinates (5,6).

b) Line segment AB, where A has coordinates (3,3) and B has coordinates (4,0).

c) Line segment RS, where R has coordinates (4,5) and S has coordinates (0,0).

d) Line segment PQ, where P has coordinates (1,3) and Q has coordinates (3,1).

e) Line segment GH, where G has coordinates (0,0) and H has coordinates (–6,–7).

Q3 Find the midpoint of each of the line segments on this graph.

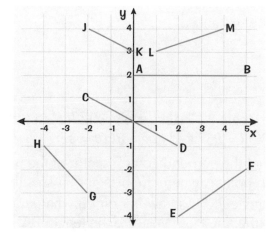

Q4 The diagram shows a cuboid. Vertices A and H have coordinates (1, 2, 8) and (4, 5, 3) respectively.

Write down the coordinates of all the other vertices.

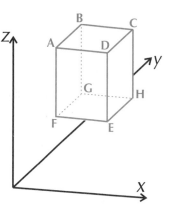

Loci and Constructions

Work through these questions bit by bit, and remember the following...

> **LOCUS** — a line showing all points obeying the given rule.
> **BISECTOR** — a line splitting an angle or line exactly in two.

Q1 **a)** Construct a triangle ABC with
AB = 4 cm, BC = 5 cm, AC = 3 cm.

b) Construct the perpendicular bisector of AB and
where this line meets BC, label the new point D.

c) Measure BD.

Q2 On a piece of paper mark two points A and B which are 6 cm apart.

a) Draw the locus of points which are 4 cm from A.

b) Draw the locus of points which are 3 cm from B.

c) There are 2 points which are both 4 cm from A and 3 cm from B.
Label them X and Y.

Q3 Draw triangle PQR accurately with length PQ = 10.5 cm,
angle PQR = 95° and angle RPQ = 32°.

a) Construct the perpendicular bisector of the line PR.
Draw in point A where the bisector crosses the line PQ.
b) Bisect angle PRQ. Draw in point B where the bisector
crosses the line PQ. Measure the length BA.

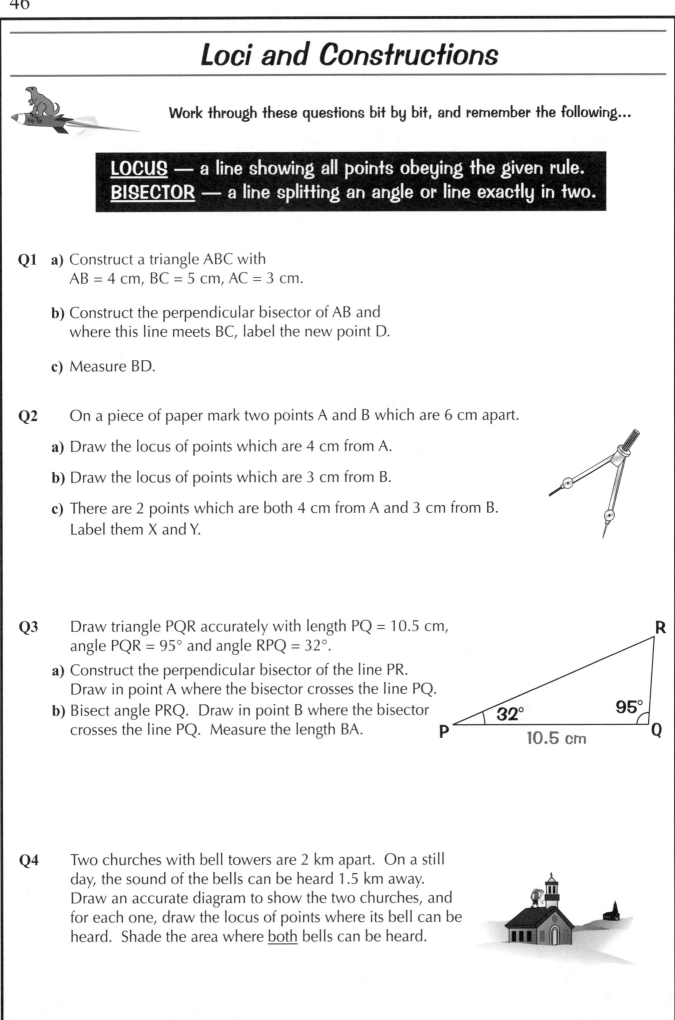

Q4 Two churches with bell towers are 2 km apart. On a still
day, the sound of the bells can be heard 1.5 km away.
Draw an accurate diagram to show the two churches, and
for each one, draw the locus of points where its bell can be
heard. Shade the area where <u>both</u> bells can be heard.

Loci and Constructions

Q5 A running track is designed so that each point on the track is 32.5 m from a fixed line AB which is 100 m long.

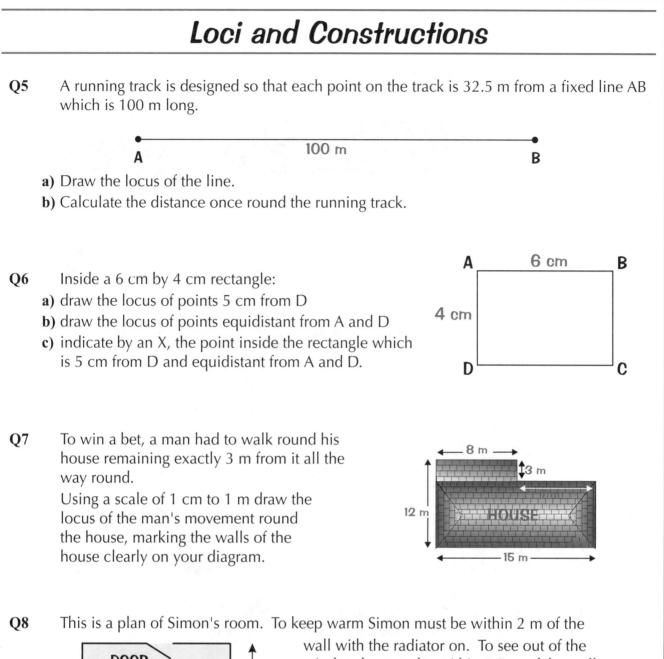

a) Draw the locus of the line.
b) Calculate the distance once round the running track.

Q6 Inside a 6 cm by 4 cm rectangle:
a) draw the locus of points 5 cm from D
b) draw the locus of points equidistant from A and D
c) indicate by an X, the point inside the rectangle which is 5 cm from D and equidistant from A and D.

Q7 To win a bet, a man had to walk round his house remaining exactly 3 m from it all the way round.
Using a scale of 1 cm to 1 m draw the locus of the man's movement round the house, marking the walls of the house clearly on your diagram.

Q8 This is a plan of Simon's room. To keep warm Simon must be within 2 m of the wall with the radiator on. To see out of the window he must be within 1.5 m of the wall containing the window.

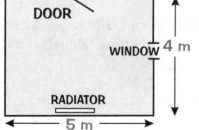

a) Using a scale of 2 cm to 1 m draw a plan of Simon's room.
b) Shade the region in which Simon must be if he is to be warm and see out of the window.

Q9 A and B are 2 points on a straight shore, 4 km apart with A due west of B.
a) Describe the locus of points P such that angle APB equals 90°.
b) Using a scale of 2 cm to 1 km draw an accurate scale diagram showing A, B, the shore line and the locus of P.
An outcrop of rock is located on a bearing of 060° from A and 300° from B.
c) Indicate the rock on your diagram. Mark the spot with an X.
d) A ship travelling from A to B follows the locus of P to avoid the rock. How near does the ship come to the rock?

Speed

This is an easy enough formula — and of course you can put it in that good old formula triangle as well.

$$\text{Average speed} = \frac{\text{Total distance}}{\text{Total time}}$$

Q1 A train travels 240 km in 4 hours. What is its <u>average speed</u>?

Q2 A car travels for 3 hours at an average speed of 55 mph. How far has it travelled?

Q3 Copy and complete this table.

Distance Travelled	Time taken	Average Speed
210 km	3 hrs	
135 miles		30 mph
	2 hrs 30 mins	42 km/h
9 miles	45 mins	
640 km		800 km/h
	1 hr 10 mins	60 mph

Q4 An athlete can run 100 m in 11 seconds. Calculate the athlete's speed in:

   a) m/s   **b)** km/h

Q5 A plane flies over city A at 09.55 and over city B at 10.02. What is its <u>average</u> speed if these cities are 63 miles apart?

Q6 The distance from Kendal (Oxenholme) to London (Euston) is 280 miles. The train travels at an average speed of 63 mph. If I catch the 07.05 from Kendal, can I be at a meeting in London by 10.30? <u>Show all your working</u>.

Q7 In a speed trial a sand yacht travelled a measured mile in 36.4 seconds.
  a) Calculate this speed in mph.
      On the return mile he took 36.16 seconds.
  b) Find his <u>total time</u> for the two runs.
  c) Calculate the average speed of the two runs in mph.

Remember, for the <u>average</u> speed, you use the <u>total</u> time and <u>total</u> distance.

Q8 A motorist drives from Manchester to London. 180 miles is on motorway where he averages 65 mph. 55 miles is on city roads where he averages 28 mph, 15 miles is on country roads where he averages 25 mph.
  a) Calculate the total time taken for the journey.
  b) How far did he travel altogether?
  c) Calculate the average speed for the journey.

Density

Here we go again — the multi-purpose formula triangle. Learn the positions of M, D and V, plug in the numbers and pull out the answer... magic.

$$\text{DENSITY} = \frac{\text{mass}}{\text{volume}}$$

Q1 Find the <u>density</u> of each of these pieces of wood, giving your answer in g/cm³:

a) Mass 3 g, volume 4 cm³

b) Mass 20 g, volume 25 cm³

c) Mass 12 kg, volume 20,000 cm³

d) Mass 14 kg, volume 0.02 m³.

Q2 Calculate the <u>mass</u> of each of these objects:

a) a small marble statue of density 2.6 g/cm³ and volume 24 cm³

b) a plastic cube of volume 64 cm³ and density 1.5 g/cm³

c) a gold ingot with density 19.5 g/cm³ measuring 12 cm by 4 cm by 4 cm

d) a pebble with volume 30 cm³ and density 2.5 g/cm³.

Q3 Work out the <u>volume</u> of each of these items:

a) a bag of sugar of mass 1 kg and density 1.6 g/cm³

b) a packet of margarine with density 2.8 g/cm³ and mass 250 g

c) a 50 kg sack of coal with density 1.8 g/cm³

d) a box of cereal with density 0.2 g/cm³ and mass 500 g.

Q4 My copper bracelet has a volume of 3.9 cm³. The density of copper is 8.9 g/cm³. Work out the <u>mass</u> of my bracelet.

Q5 Ice has a density of 0.93 g/cm³. If the mass of a block of ice is 19.5 kg, what is its <u>volume</u>?

Q6 Some petrol in a can has a mass of 4 kg. The density of the petrol is 0.8 g/cm³. How many <u>litres</u> of petrol are in the can? 1 litre = 1000 cm³.

Q7 A jug holds 1.9 litres of lemonade. The mass of the lemonade is 2 kg. Find the <u>density</u> of the lemonade.

Q8 A 1.5 kg bag full of self raising flour measures 12 cm by 18 cm by 6 cm. A 1 kg bag of granary flour measures 10 cm by 14 cm by 6 cm. Find the <u>density</u> of each sort of flour.

Probability

So the probability is that you don't want to do two pages of probability questions. But the feeling of smug satisfaction when you've completed them will make it all worthwhile, believe me. This first page is on <u>calculating probabilities</u>.

Q1 Write down, as a fraction, the probability of these events happening:

a) Throwing a 5 with an unbiased six-sided dice.

b) Drawing a red card from a pack of cards.

c) Drawing a king from a pack of cards.

d) Throwing a 0 with a dice.

Q2 One letter is chosen from the word '**MILITARY**'. What is the probability that the letter is:

a) an R?

b) an I?

c) a vowel?

> All you need to know for part a) is how many Rs there are and how many letters altogether.

Q3 The number of pets owned by ten people are shown below.

$$2, \ 0, \ 0, \ 1, \ 4, \ 5, \ 3, \ 6, \ 1, \ 0$$

One of the people is chosen at random. Calculate the probability that they own:

a) 2 pets   **b)** more than 3 pets

Q4 The chance of rain is forecast to be 38%.
a) What is the probability of it <u>not</u> raining?
b) Which is <u>more likely</u> — rain or no rain?

Q5 A rugby squad consists of 30 players. Only 15 players can start the game and only 4 substitutes are allowed. If the players are chosen at random, work out the probability that Alan will <u>not</u> be chosen to <u>play or be a substitute</u>.

Q6 Students at school conduct a survey of the colours of parents' cars. The table show the results.

Red	Blue	Yellow	White	Green	Other
40	29	13	20	16	14

One of the cars is picked at random.

a) What is the probability of it being a <u>red</u> car?
b) What is the probability that the car is <u>neither blue nor green</u>?

Probability — Relative Frequency

You also need to be able to <u>estimate</u> probabilities for module 7. Here goes...

Q1 **a)** A biased dice is rolled 40 times. A six came up 14 times.
Calculate the relative frequency that a six was rolled.

b) The same dice is rolled another 60 times. From this, a six came up 24 times.
Calculate the relative frequency that a six was rolled.

c) Use the data from **a)** and **b)** to make the best estimate you
can of the probability of rolling a six with the dice.

Remember — the more times you do an experiment, the more accurate it will be.

Q2 Joe spins this spinner 100 times, and gets the following results:

Score	1	2	3	4
Frequency	18	20	40	22

Estimate the probability of getting a '2' with Joe's spinner.

Q3 The notepad below shows orders for 4 different sorts of rice at a certain Indian
restaurant. Based on this data, estimate the probability that the next order of rice is:

boiled	20
pilau	24
spicy mushroom	10
special fried	6

a) for pilau rice

b) for spicy mushroom or special fried rice

c) not for boiled rice

If you're asked to work out probabilities based on some data, it's a <u>relative frequency</u> question.

Q4 Carla wants to estimate the league position her local dominos
team will finish in this year. This graph shows the number of
times they have finished in each position over the last 50 years:

a) Estimate the probabilities of the team finishing in each of
the six positions this year.

b) What position is the team most likely to finish in this year? Explain your answer.

Q5 Imagine you have just made a 6-sided spinner in Design and Technology.
How could you test whether or not it's a fair spinner?

Remember — if the spinner's fair, the probability of landing on each side is the same.

Go veggie, go veggie...

Oi, this isn't fair...

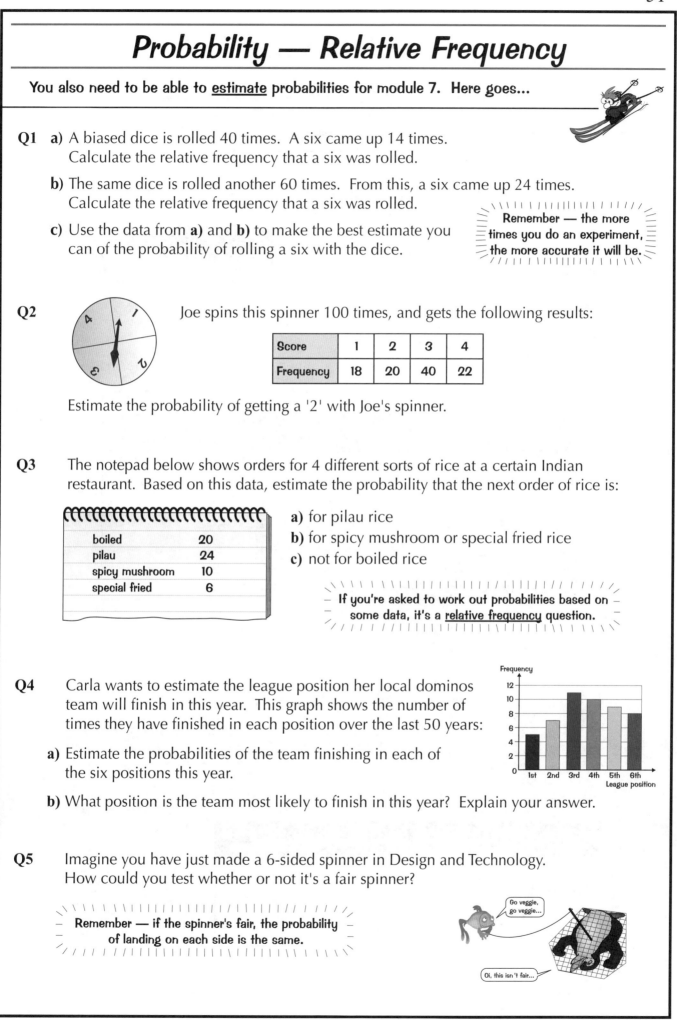

Grouped Frequency Tables

First things first, do <u>page 23</u> on standard frequency tables.
Done that? Good. Now here are some trickier questions,
where you have to <u>estimate</u> the mean using mid-interval values.

Q1 In a survey of test results in a French class at Blugdon High,
these grades were achieved by the 23 pupils:

a) Write down the mid-interval values
for each of the groups.

(grade) score	(E) 31-40	(D) 41-50	(C) 51-60	(B) 61-70
frequency	4	7	8	4

b) Calculate an estimate for the mean value.

Q2 This table shows times for each team of swimmers, the Dolphins and the Sharks.

Dolphins			Sharks		
Time interval (seconds)	Frequency	Mid-interval value	Time interval (seconds)	Frequency	Mid-interval value
$14 \leq t < 20$	3	17	$14 \leq t < 20$	6	17
$20 \leq t < 26$	7	23	$20 \leq t < 26$	15	23
$26 \leq t < 32$	15		$26 \leq t < 32$	33	
$32 \leq t < 38$	32		$32 \leq t < 38$	59	
$38 \leq t < 44$	45		$38 \leq t < 44$	20	
$44 \leq t < 50$	30		$44 \leq t < 50$	8	
$50 \leq t < 56$	5		$50 \leq t < 56$	2	

a) Copy and complete the table, writing in all mid-interval values.
b) Use the mid-interval technique to estimate the mean time for each team.

Q3 The weights in kg of 18 newly felled trees are noted below:

272.7	333.2	251.0	246.5	328.0	259.6	200.2	312.8
344.3	226.8	362.0	348.3	256.1	232.9	309.7	398.0
284.5	327.4						

a) Copy and complete the frequency table.

Weight (kg)	Tally	Frequency	Mid-Interval	Frequency × Mid-Interval
$200 \leq w < 250$				
$250 \leq w < 300$				
$300 \leq w < 350$				
$350 \leq w < 400$				

Have you seen Ron?

b) Estimate the mean weight using the frequency table.
c) What is the modal group?

Scatter Graphs

The big word you're supposed to use in these questions is <u>correlation</u> — and they're very keen on it, so make sure you know what it means.

Q1 The scattergraphs below show the relationship between:

a) The temperature of the day and the amount of ice cream sold.

b) The price of ice cream and the amount sold.

c) The age of customers and the amount of ice cream sold.

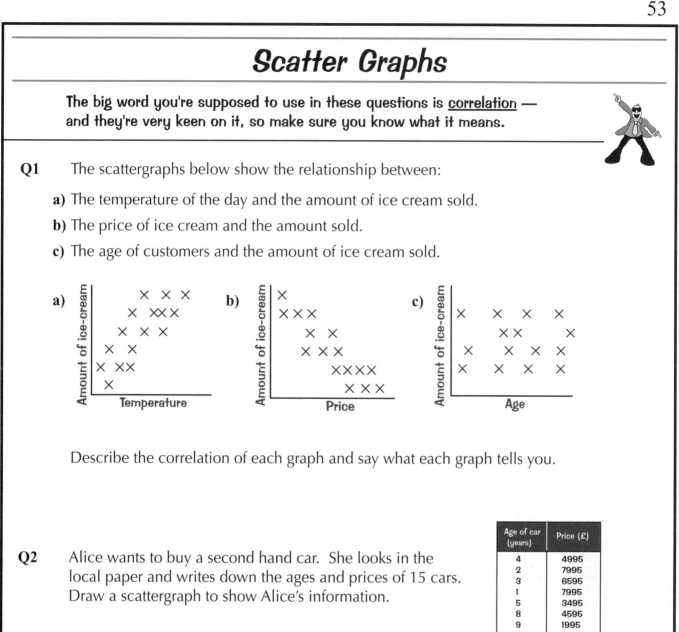

Describe the correlation of each graph and say what each graph tells you.

Q2 Alice wants to buy a second hand car. She looks in the local paper and writes down the ages and prices of 15 cars. Draw a scattergraph to show Alice's information.

What does the scattergraph tell you about the relationship between the age of a car and its price?

Age of car (years)	Price (£)
4	4995
2	7995
3	6595
1	7995
5	3495
8	4595
9	1995
1	7695
2	7795
6	3995
5	3995
1	9195
3	5995
4	4195
9	2195

Q3 The table below shows the masses of 12 fathers and their eldest sons.

Mass of Father (kg)	65	71	67	69	67	63	62	70	66	68	68	64
Mass of son (kg)	68	70	67	68	68	66	66	68	65	71	69	65

a) Construct a scatter graph to show this information.

b) Draw a line of best fit.

c) Use your line of best fit to predict the mass of a son for a father whose mass is 61 kg.

MODULE 8

Standard Index Form

Writing very big (or very small) numbers gets a bit messy with all those zeros if you don't use this standard index form. But of course, the main reason for knowing about standard form is... you guessed it — it's in the Exam.

Q1 Write as ordinary numbers:

a) 3.56×10 e) 0.082×10^2 i) 157×10

b) 3.56×10^3 f) 0.082×10^{-2} j) 157×10^{-3}

c) 3.56×10^{-1} g) 0.082×10 k) 157×10^3

d) 3.56×10^4 h) 0.082×10^{-1} l) 157×10^{-1}

Q2 Write in standard form:

a) 2.56   e) 95.2   i) 4200

b) 25.6   f) 0.0952   j) 0.0042

c) 0.256   g) 95 200   k) 42

d) 25 600   h) 0.000952   l) 420

Q3 Write in standard form:

a) 34.7×10 e) 15 million   i) 534×10^{-2}

b) 73.004   f) 937.1×10^4 j) 621.03

c) 0.005×10^3 g) 0.000075   k) 149×10^2

d) 9183×10^2 h) 0.05×10^{-2} l) 0.003×10^{-4}

Write the numbers in Questions 4 to 7 in standard form.

Q4 The distance between Paris and Rome is 1476 km.

Q5 A billion = a thousand million   A trillion = a thousand billion.

Q6 A light year is 9,460,000,000,000 km (approx).

Q7 Nautilus covered 69,138 miles before having to refuel.

Q8 A rectangular field is 24,700 cm by 15,000 cm.
What is its perimeter in m? Give your answer in standard form.

Q9 This table gives the diameter and distance from the Sun of some planets.

Planet	Distance from Sun (km)	Diameter (km)
Earth	1.5×10^8	1.3×10^4
Venus	1.085×10^8	1.2×10^4
Mars	2.28×10^8	6.8×10^3
Mercury	5.81×10^7	4.9×10^3
Jupiter	7.8×10^8	1.4×10^5
Neptune	4.52×10^9	4.9×10^4
Saturn	1.43×10^9	1.2×10^5

From the table write down which planet is:

a) smallest in diameter

b) largest in diameter

c) nearest to the Sun

d) furthest from the Sun.

Write down which planets are:

e) nearer to the Sun than the Earth

f) bigger in diameter than the Earth.

Standard Index Form

This stuff gets a lot easier if you know how to handle your calculator — read and learn.

Standard Index Form with a Calculator

Use the **EXP** button (or **EE** button) to enter numbers in standard index form.

Eg $1.7 \times 10^9 + 2.6 \times 10^{10}$ ☐**1** ☐**.** ☐**7** **EXP** ☐**9** **+** ☐**2** ☐**.** ☐**6** **EXP** **10** **=**

The answer is 〔 2.77^{10} 〕 which is read as 2.77×10^{10}

Q10 Which is <u>greater</u>, 4.62×10^{12} or 1.04×10^{13}, and <u>by how much</u>?

Q11 Which is <u>smaller</u> 3.2×10^{-8} or 1.3×10^{-9} and by how much?

Q12 The following numbers are <u>not</u> written in standard index form.
Rewrite them correctly using standard index form.

a) 42×10^6 **d)** 11.2×10^{-5} **g)** 17×10^{17}
b) 38×10^{-5} **e)** 843×10^3 **h)** 28.3×10^{-5}
c) 10×10^6 **f)** 42.32×10^{-4} **i)** 10×10^{-3}

Don't forget — when you're using a calculator, you've got to write the answer as 3.46×10^{27}, <u>not</u> as 3.46^{27}. If you do it the wrong way, it means something <u>completely</u> different.

Q13 What is <u>7 million</u> in standard index form?

Q14 The radius of the Earth is 6.38×10^3 km. What is the radius of the Earth measured in <u>cm</u>? Leave your answer in standard form.

Q15 One atomic mass unit is equivalent to 1.661×10^{-27} kg. What are <u>two</u> atomic mass units equivalent to (in standard index form)?

Q16 The length of a light year, the distance light can travel in one year, is 9.461×10^{15} m. How far can light travel in:
a) 2 years?
b) 6 months?
Write your answers in <u>standard form</u>.

Q17 a) The surface area of the Earth is approximately 5.1×10^8 km². Write this <u>without</u> using standard form.
b) The area of the Earth covered by sea is 362 000 000 km². Write this in standard form.
c) What is the approximate area of the Earth covered by land? Write your answer <u>without</u> using standard form.

Percentage Problems

Q1 Kate paid £3500 for a classic sports car.
Each year its value decreased by 8%.

a) How much was it worth after one year?

b) How much was it worth after three years?

Q2 Denzel buys a baby pygmy goat for £1500. The value of the goat decreases by 10% in its first year. Each year after that the goat decreases in value by 20%. What is the value of the goat after 4 years?

Q3 During a rainstorm, a water butt increased in weight from 10.4 kg to 13.6 kg. What was the percentage increase (to the nearest percent)?

> When you're finding percentage increase or decrease, remember to divide by the original value.

Q4 An electrical store reduces the price of a particular camera from £90.00 to £78.30. What is the percentage reduction?

Q5 At birth, Veronica was 0.3 m tall. By adulthood she had grown to 1.5 m tall. Calculate her height now as a percentage of her height at birth.

Q6 Robin bought a penguin-resistant tennis racket for £68.00 in a sale. The original price had been reduced by 15%. What was the original price?

Q7 A pair of jeans shrunk in length by 20% after washing.
a) If the jeans are now 32 inches long, how long were they originally?
b) If the jeans are now 28 inches long, how long were they originally?

Q8 Janet bought a new hat in the sales for £42.00. The original price had been reduced by 25%. What was the original price?

Q9 There are 360 people living in a certain village.
The population of the village has grown by 20% over the past year.
a) How many people lived in the village one year ago?
b) If the village continues to grow at the same rate, how many whole years from today will it be before the population is more than twice its current size?

> If you're still peckish for more percentage practice, have a peek back at page **29**. There's plenty of pesky problems there to perk you up.

Basic Algebra

Q1 Multiply out the brackets and simplify where possible:

a) $4e(e + 2f) + 2f(e - f)$

b) $4x(x + 2) - 2x(3 - x)$

c) $3(2 + ab) + 5(1 - ab)$

d) $(x - 2y)z - 2x(x + z)$

e) $4pq(2 + r) + 5qr(2p + 7)$

f) $x^2(x + 1)$

g) $4x^2\left(x + 2 + \dfrac{1}{x}\right)$

h) $8ab(a + 3 + b)$

i) $7pq\left(p + q - \dfrac{1}{p}\right)$

Remember <u>FOIL</u> for multiplying brackets... don't want to miss any terms now, do you...

Q2 Multiply out the brackets and simplify your answers where possible:

a) $(x - 3)(x + 1)$

b) $(x - 3)(x + 5)$

c) $(x + 10)(x + 3)$

d) $(x - 5)(x - 2)$

e) $(x + 2)(x - 7)$

f) $(4 - x)(7 - x)$

g) $(2 + 3x)(3x - 1)$

h) $(3x + 2)(2x - 4)$

i) $(x - 3)(4x + 1)$

j) $2(2x + y)(x - 2y)$

k) $4(x + 2y)(3x - 2y)$

l) $(3x + 2y)^2$

Q3 Find the product of $5x - 2$ and $3x + 2$.

Q4 Find the square of $2x - 1$.

Q5 A rectangular pond has length $(3x - 2)$ m and width $(5 - x)$ m.
Write down a simplified expression for:

a) the pond's perimeter

b) the pond's area.

Q6 Find a simplified expression for the perimeter *and* the area of the following shapes.

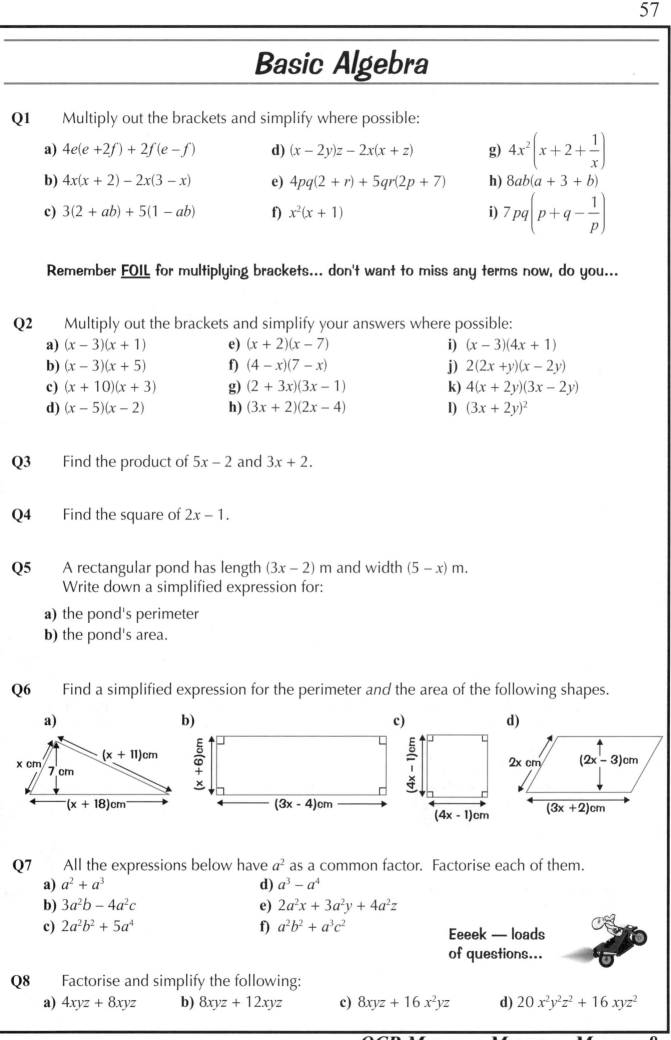

Q7 All the expressions below have a^2 as a common factor. Factorise each of them.

a) $a^2 + a^3$

b) $3a^2b - 4a^2c$

c) $2a^2b^2 + 5a^4$

d) $a^3 - a^4$

e) $2a^2x + 3a^2y + 4a^2z$

f) $a^2b^2 + a^3c^2$

Eeeek — loads of questions...

Q8 Factorise and simplify the following:

a) $4xyz + 8xyz$

b) $8xyz + 12xyz$

c) $8xyz + 16 x^2yz$

d) $20 x^2y^2z^2 + 16 xyz^2$

Solving Equations

Q1 Solve:
a) $2(x-3)-(x-2)=5$
b) $5(x+2)-3(x-5)=29$
c) $2(x+2)+3(x+4)=31$
d) $10(x+3)-4(x-2)=7(x+5)$
e) $5(4x+3)=4(7x-5)+3(9-2x)$
f) $3(7+2x)+2(1-x)=19$

g) $\dfrac{x}{3}+7=12$

h) $\dfrac{x}{10}+18=29$

i) $17-\dfrac{x^2}{3}=5$

j) $41-\dfrac{x}{11}=35$

k) $\dfrac{x}{100}-3=4$

l) $\dfrac{120}{x}=16$

Q2 For what value of x is the expression $14-\dfrac{x}{2}$ equal to the value $\dfrac{3x-4}{2}$?

It's easy — you just put the 2 bits together and there's your equation. Then all you've got to do is solve it...

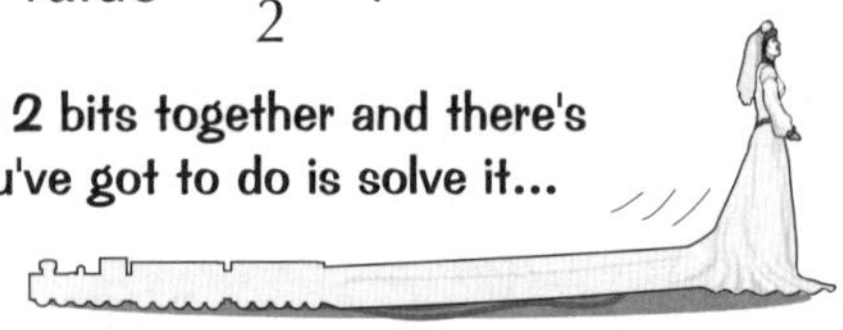

Q3 Solve the following:

a) $\dfrac{y}{2}+2=13$

b) $\dfrac{3x}{4}-2=4$

c) $\dfrac{2z}{5}-3=-5$

d) $\dfrac{1}{5}(x-4)=3$

e) $\dfrac{2}{3}(x+1)=16$

f) $\dfrac{3}{5}(4x-3)=15$

g) $\dfrac{8}{x^2}=\dfrac{32}{36}$

h) $\dfrac{12}{5x^2}=\dfrac{3}{20}$

i) $\dfrac{14}{3x^2}=\dfrac{2}{21}$

Q4 Solve the following:

a) $\dfrac{4x+3}{2}+x=\dfrac{5x+41}{4}$

Remember to do the same to the top and the bottom.

b) $\dfrac{5}{7}(x-2)-\dfrac{3}{4}(x+3)=-4$

Q5 Joan, Kate and Linda win £2400 on the National Lottery between them. Joan gets a share of £x, whilst Kate gets twice as much as Joan. Linda's share is £232 less than Joan's amount.
a) Write down an expression for the amounts Joan, Kate and Linda win.
b) Write down an expression in terms of x, and solve it.
c) Write down the amounts Kate and Linda receive.

Q6 All the angles in the diagram are right angles.
a) Write down an expression for the perimeter of the shape.
b) Write down an expression for the area of the shape.
c) For what value of x will the perimeter and area be numerically equal?

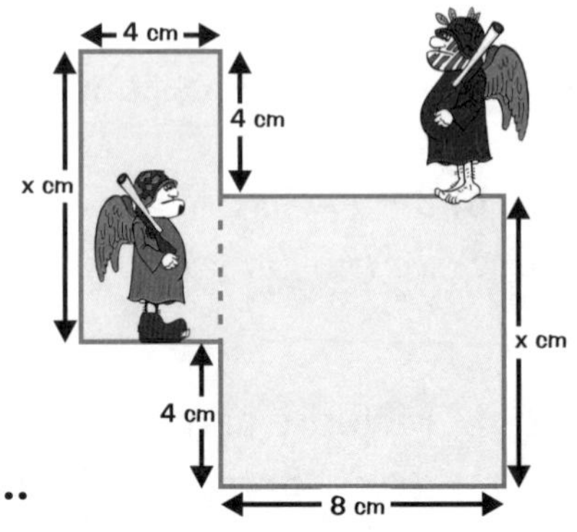

Big blobs and broomsticks...

4 cm

4 cm

x cm

4 cm

x cm

8 cm

Rearranging Formulas

If you want some easier formula questions to warm up on before you start this page, have a look back at p34-35 of module 7.

Q1 Rearrange the following formulas to make the letter in brackets the new subject.

a) $g = 10 - 4h$ (h)

e) $f = \dfrac{3g}{8}$ (g)

b) $d = \frac{1}{2}(c + 4)$ (c)

f) $y = \dfrac{x}{2} - 3$ (x)

c) $j = -2(3 - k)$ (k)

g) $s = \dfrac{t}{6} + 10$ (t)

d) $a = \dfrac{2b}{3}$ (b)

h) $p = 4q^2$ (q)

Q2 Rearrange the following formulas to make the letter in brackets the new subject.

a) $y = x^2 - 2$ (x)

d) $f = \dfrac{10 + g}{3}$ (g)

g) $v^2 = u^2 + 2as$ (a)

b) $y = \sqrt{(x + 3)}$ (x)

e) $w = \dfrac{5 - z}{2}$ (z)

h) $v^2 = u^2 + 2as$ (u)

c) $y = \left(\dfrac{s}{2}\right)^2$ (s)

f) $v = \dfrac{1}{3}x^2 h$ (x)

i) $t = 2\pi\sqrt{\dfrac{l}{g}}$ (g)

Q3 Rearrange the following formulas, by collecting terms in x and looking for common factors, to make x the new subject.

a) $xy = z - 2x$

e) $xy = xz - 2$

b) $ax = 3x + b$

f) $2(x - y) = z(x + 3)$

c) $4x - y = xz$

g) $xyz = x - y - wz$

d) $xy = 3z - 5x + y$

h) $3y(x + z) = y(2z - x)$

Q4 Mrs Smith buys x jumpers for £J each and sells them in her shop for a total price of £T.
a) Write down an expression for the amount of money she paid for all the jumpers.
b) Using your answer to **a)**, write down a formula for the profit £P Mrs Smith makes selling all the jumpers.
c) Rearrange the formula to make J the subject.
d) Given that Mrs Smith makes a profit of £156 by selling 13 jumpers for a total of £364 find the price she paid for each jumper originally.

Q5 The cost of developing a film is 12p per print plus 60p postage.

a) Write down a formula for the cost C, in pence, of developing x prints.

b) Rearrange the formula to make x the subject.

c) Find the number of prints developed when a customer is charged:

    i) £4.92   **ii)** £6.36   **iii)** £12.12.

Simultaneous Equations

To solve simultaneous equations from scratch, you've got to get rid of either x or y first — to leave you with an equation with just one unknown in it.

Q1 Eliminate either the x term or the y term by adding or subtracting the pairs of equations and hence solve the equations:

a) $4x - y = 13$
$2x - y = 5$

b) $8x + 3y = 8$
$5x - 3y = 5$

c) $x + 3y = 10$
$2x - 3y = 2$

d) $8x + 6y = 2$
$2(x - 3y) = 3$

e) $x - 12y = 16$
$5x + 12y = 8$

f) $2(5x - y + 4) = 0$
$10x + y = 19$

g) $11x + 3y = 5$
$7x - 3y = 13$

h) $2x + 7y = 11$
$2x + 3y = 7$

i) $x + 6y = 5$
$3(x + 2y - 1) = 0$

How do you solve a problem like 2x + y = 2, 3x − y = 14?

Q2 Use elimination to solve these equations. Start by multiplying one equation by a number and then adding or subtracting.

By elimination.

a) $3x + 2y = 12$
$2x + y = 7$

b) $5x - y = 17$
$2x + 3y = 0$

c) $x + 3y = 11$
$2x + 5y = 19$

d) $5x + 3y = 24$
$x + 5y = -4$

e) $3x + 2y = 3$
$2x + y = 23$

f) $4x + 2y = 8$
$x + 3y = 2$

g) $x + 14y = -2$
$2x + 3y = 21$

h) $3x + 2y = 21$
$2x - y = 7$

i) $4x - y = -2$
$3x - 2y = 1$

Q3 Multiply both equations by a number before adding or subtracting, to solve these:

a) $7y - 3x = 2$
$5y - 2x = 2$

b) $5x - 8y = 12$
$4x - 7y = 9$

c) $4x - 2y = -6$
$5x + 3y = 20$

d) $7x + 5y = 66$
$3x - 4y = 16$

e) $10x + 4y = 2$
$8x + 3y = 1$

f) $3x + 4y = 19$
$4x - 3y = -8$

Q4 A farmer has a choice of buying 6 sheep and 5 pigs for £430 or 4 sheep and 10 pigs for £500 at auction.

a) If sheep cost £x and pigs cost £y, write down his two choices as a pair of simultaneous equations.

b) Solve for x and y.

Q5 Six apples and four oranges cost £1.90, whereas eight apples and two oranges cost £1.80. Find the cost of an apple and the cost of an orange.

Q6 Find the value of x and y for each of the following rectangles, by first writing down a pair of simultaneous equations and then solving them.

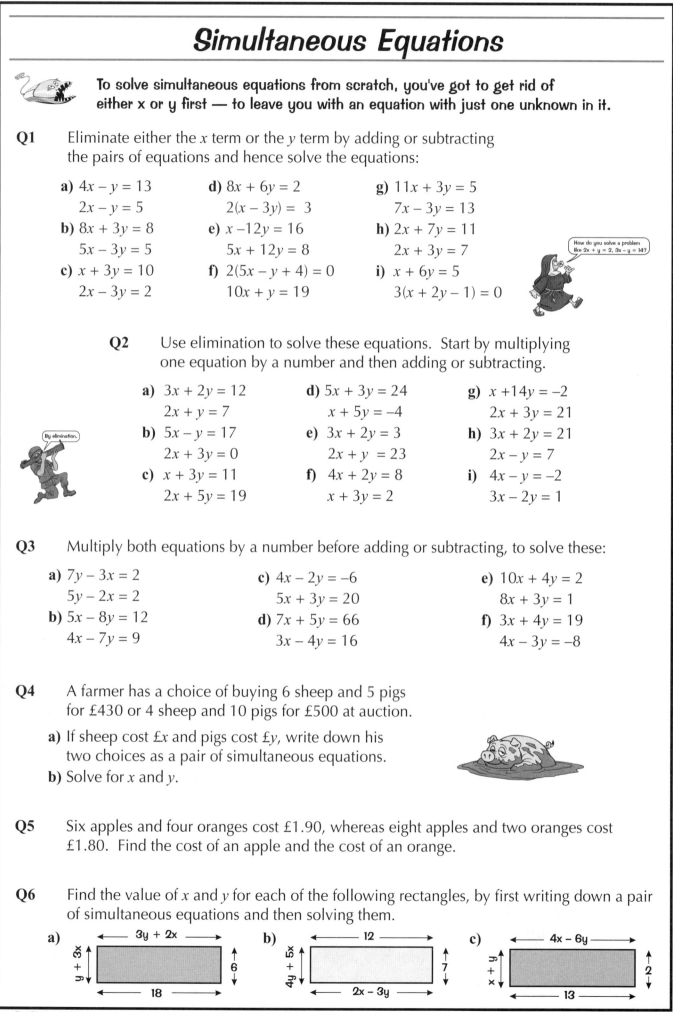

a) top: $3y + 2x$; bottom: 18; left side: $y + 3x$; right side: 6

b) top: 12; bottom: $2x - 3y$; left side: $4y + 5x$; right side: 7

c) top: $4x - 6y$; bottom: 13; left side: $y + x$; right side: 2

Simultaneous Equations with Graphs

Q1 Solve these simultaneous equations by looking at the graphs.
Then check your answers by substituting the values back into the equations.

a) $y + 2x = 9$
$3y = x + 6$

b) $y = x + 6$
$3y + x = 18$

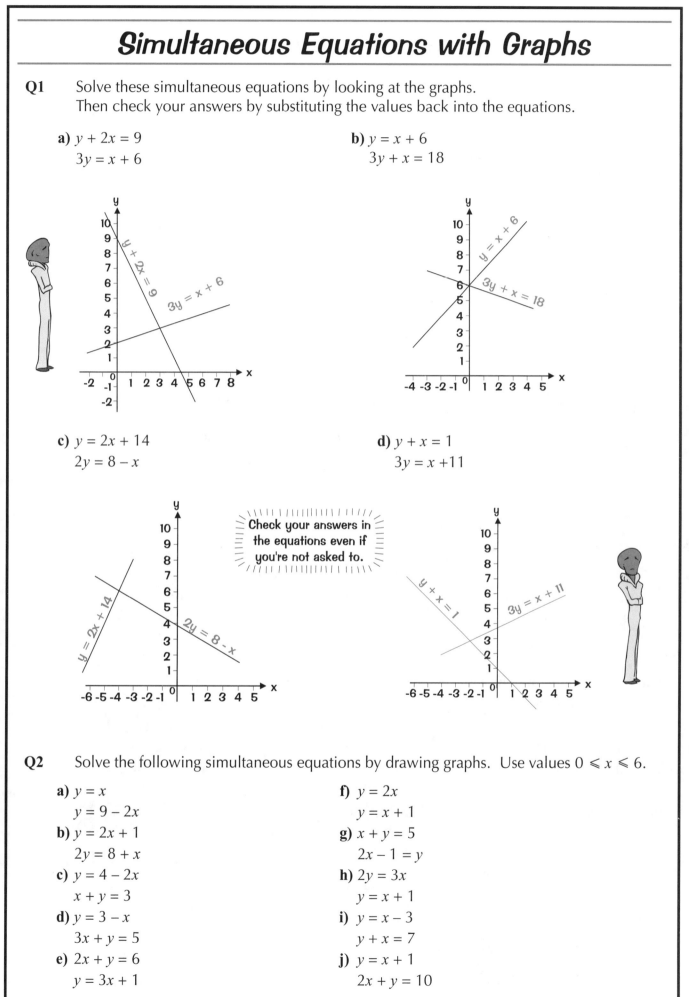

c) $y = 2x + 14$
$2y = 8 - x$

d) $y + x = 1$
$3y = x + 11$

Check your answers in the equations even if you're not asked to.

Q2 Solve the following simultaneous equations by drawing graphs. Use values $0 \leqslant x \leqslant 6$.

a) $y = x$
$y = 9 - 2x$

b) $y = 2x + 1$
$2y = 8 + x$

c) $y = 4 - 2x$
$x + y = 3$

d) $y = 3 - x$
$3x + y = 5$

e) $2x + y = 6$
$y = 3x + 1$

f) $y = 2x$
$y = x + 1$

g) $x + y = 5$
$2x - 1 = y$

h) $2y = 3x$
$y = x + 1$

i) $y = x - 3$
$y + x = 7$

j) $y = x + 1$
$2x + y = 10$

Quadratic Equations

The "Difference Of Two Squares" (D.O.T.S.) is a handy factorising rule:

$$a^2 - b^2 = (a + b)(a - b)$$

It's bound to be in your exam — the big trick is spotting when to use it.

Q1 Use D.O.T.S. to factorise the following expressions:

a) $x^2 - 9$ d) $36 - a^2$ g) $49x^4y^4 - 1$ j) $x^4 - y^4$

b) $y^2 - 16$ e) $4x^2 - 9$ h) $1 - 36a^2$ k) $1 - (ab)^2$

c) $25 - z^2$ f) $9y^2 - 4$ i) $1 - 9x^2y^2$ l) $100\,x^2 - 144y^2$

Q2 Factorise and hence solve the following equations:

a) $x^2 - 4 = 0$ b) $81 - y^2 = 0$ c) $9x^2 - 36$ d) $25 - 16z^2$

Q3 Factorise and hence solve $4x^2 - \frac{1}{4} = 0$.

Equations with an x^2 term in are called quadratic equations. They can be written as "$ax^2 + bx + c = 0$", where a, b and c are numbers. The easiest way to solve them is by <u>factorising</u>...

Q4 Factorise the following:

a) $x^2 + x - 6$ c) $x^2 - 2x - 35$ e) $x^2 - 3x - 54$

b) $x^2 - x - 12$ d) $x^2 - 4x - 32$ f) $x^2 - 5x + 6$

Q5 Factorise the quadratics first, and then solve the equations:

a) $x^2 + 3x - 10 = 0$ d) $x^2 - 4x + 3 = 0$ g) $x^2 + 6x - 7 = 0$

b) $x^2 - 5x + 6 = 0$ e) $x^2 - x - 20 = 0$ h) $x^2 + 14x + 49 = 0$

c) $x^2 - 2x + 1 = 0$ f) $x^2 - 4x - 5 = 0$ i) $x^2 - 2x - 15 = 0$

Q6 Rearrange into the form $x^2 + bx + c = 0$, then solve by factorising:

a) $x^2 - 2x = 15$ e) $x^2 + 5x = 36$ i) $x^2 = 7x$

b) $x^2 + 5x = 14$ f) $x^2 + 4x = 45$ j) $x^2 = 11x$

c) $x^2 + 6x = 16$ g) $x^2 - 3x = 10$ k) $x^2 - 21 = 4x$

d) $x^2 + 4x = 21$ h) $x^2 = 5x$ l) $x^2 - 63 = 2x$

Q7 The area of a rectangular swimming pool is 28 m². The width is x m. The difference between the length and width is 3 m. Form a quadratic equation and solve it to find the value of x.

x m

Q8 A rug has length x m. The width is exactly 1 m less than the length.

a) Write down an expression for the area of the rug.

b) If the area of the rug is 6 m², find the value of x.

xm

Inequalities

Q1 Solve the following:

a) $3x + 2 > 11$ e) $2x - 7 \geq 8$ i) $5(x + 2) \geq 25$ m) $8 - 3x \geq 14$

b) $5x + 4 < 24$ f) $17 + 4x < 33$ j) $4(x - 1) > 40$ n) $16 - x < 11$

c) $5x + 7 \leq 32$ g) $2(x + 3) < 20$ k) $10 - 2x > 4x - 8$ o) $16 - x > 1$

d) $3x + 12 \leq 30$ h) $2(5x - 4) < 32$ l) $7 - 2x \leq 4x + 10$ p) $12 - 3x \leq 18$

Q2 Find the largest integer x, such that $2x + 5 \geq 5x - 2$.

Q3 When a number is subtracted from 11, and this new number is then divided by two, the result is always less than five. Write this information as an inequality and solve it to show the possible values of the number.

There's plenty more practice on "normal" inequalities on page 37 from module 7.

Q4 A person is prepared to spend £300 taking friends out for a meal. If the restaurant charges £12 per head, how many guests could be invited? Show this information as an inequality.

For graphical inequalities you need to be happy drawing straight line graphs from equations. If you're a bit rusty, look at pages 9 or 64-65.

Q5 The shaded region satisfies three inequalities. Write down these inequalities.

Remember the difference between solid and dotted lines.

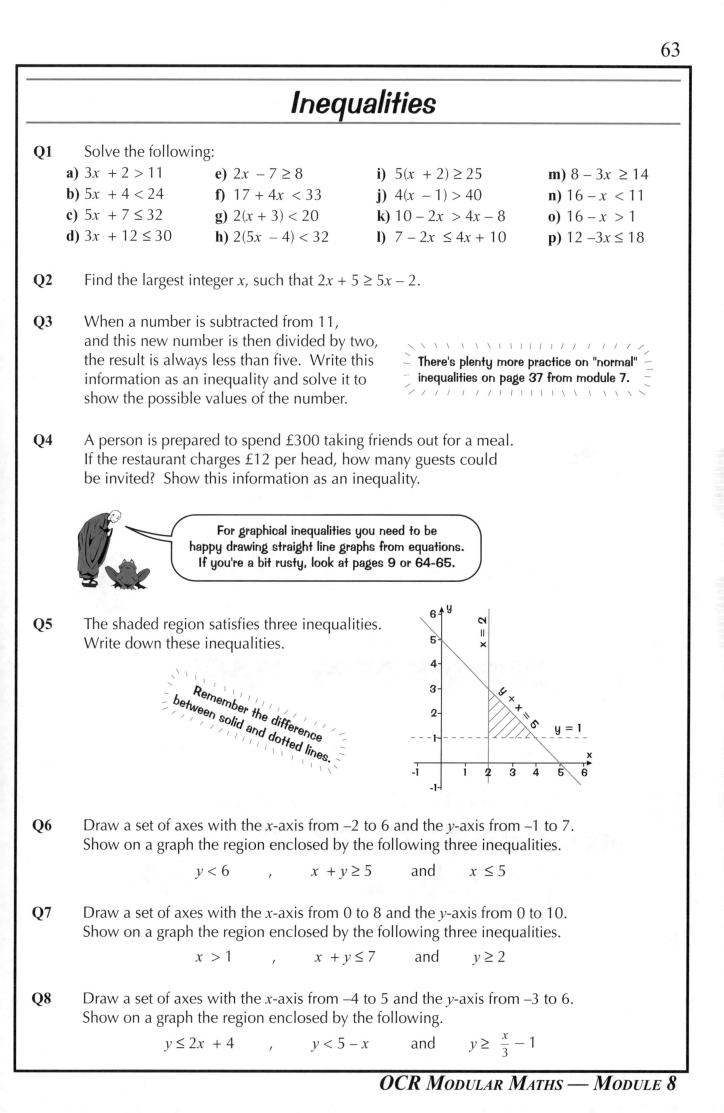

Q6 Draw a set of axes with the x-axis from –2 to 6 and the y-axis from –1 to 7. Show on a graph the region enclosed by the following three inequalities.

$$y < 6 \quad , \quad x + y \geq 5 \quad \text{and} \quad x \leq 5$$

Q7 Draw a set of axes with the x-axis from 0 to 8 and the y-axis from 0 to 10. Show on a graph the region enclosed by the following three inequalities.

$$x > 1 \quad , \quad x + y \leq 7 \quad \text{and} \quad y \geq 2$$

Q8 Draw a set of axes with the x-axis from –4 to 5 and the y-axis from –3 to 6. Show on a graph the region enclosed by the following.

$$y \leq 2x + 4 \quad , \quad y < 5 - x \quad \text{and} \quad y \geq \frac{x}{3} - 1$$

Straight Line Graphs

Q1 Write down the letter that represents each of the following equations:

a) $x = y$
b) $x = 5$
c) $y = -x$
d) $x = 0$
e) $y = -7$
f) $x + y = 0$
g) $y = 5$
h) $x - y = 0$
i) $y = 0$
j) $x = -7$

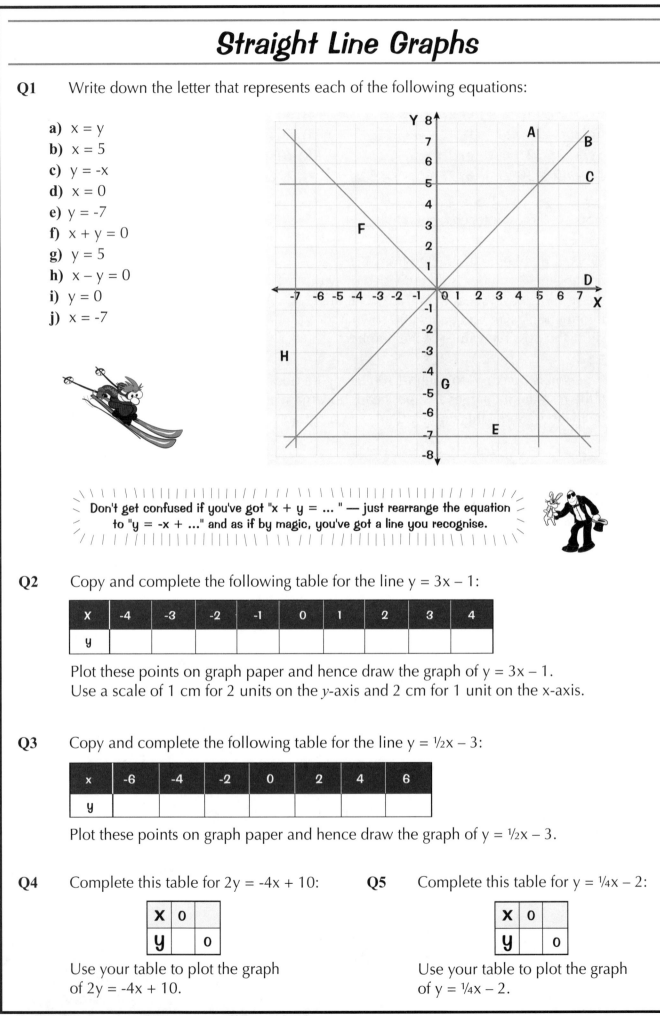

Don't get confused if you've got "x + y = ... " — just rearrange the equation to "y = -x + ..." and as if by magic, you've got a line you recognise.

Q2 Copy and complete the following table for the line $y = 3x - 1$:

X	-4	-3	-2	-1	0	1	2	3	4
y									

Plot these points on graph paper and hence draw the graph of $y = 3x - 1$.
Use a scale of 1 cm for 2 units on the *y*-axis and 2 cm for 1 unit on the x-axis.

Q3 Copy and complete the following table for the line $y = \frac{1}{2}x - 3$:

x	-6	-4	-2	0	2	4	6
y							

Plot these points on graph paper and hence draw the graph of $y = \frac{1}{2}x - 3$.

Q4 Complete this table for $2y = -4x + 10$:

X	0	
y		0

Use your table to plot the graph of $2y = -4x + 10$.

Q5 Complete this table for $y = \frac{1}{4}x - 2$:

X	0	
y		0

Use your table to plot the graph of $y = \frac{1}{4}x - 2$.

Straight Lines — y = mx + c

Writing the equation of a line in the form y = mx + c gives you a __nifty way__ to find the __gradient__ and __y-intercept__. Remember that — it'll save you loads of time. Anything for an easy life...

Q1 For each of the following lines, give the gradient and the coordinates of the point where the line cuts the *y*-axis.

a) $y = 4x + 3$

b) $y = 3x - 2$

c) $y = 2x + 1$

d) $y = -3x + 3$

e) $y = 5x$

f) $y = -2x + 3$

g) $y = -6x - 4$

h) $y = x$

i) $y = -\frac{1}{2}x + 3$

j) $y = \frac{1}{4}x + 2$

k) $3y = 4x + 6$

l) $2y = -5x - 4$

m) $8y = 4x - 12$

n) $3y = 7x + 5$

o) $x + y = 0$

p) $x - y = 0$

q) $y - x = 3$

r) $x - 3 = y$

s) $y - 7 = 3x$

t) $y - 5x = 3$

u) $y + 2x + 3 = 0$

v) $y =$ 🐑$x + 2$🐑

Q2 Find the values for m and c if the linear graph y = mx + c has a gradient of 3 and passes through (0, 8).

Q3 Find the values for m and c if the linear graph y = mx + c has a gradient of 1 and passes through (2, 0).

Q4 a) Find the gradient and y-intercept for the line 3y = 6x + 15.
b) Hence draw the graph of 3y = 6x + 15 for values of x between -2 and 4.

> Mark the y-intercept, then use the gradient to draw the line in both directions.

Q5 a) Find the gradient and y-intercept for the line 2y + 2x = 16.
b) Hence draw the graph of 2y + 2x = 16 for values of x between -2 and 4.

Q6 a) Find the gradient and y-intercept for the line 4y - 2x + 4 = 0.
b) Hence draw the graph of 4y - 2x + 4 = 0 for values of x between -2 and 4.

Straight Lines — Gradients

The gradient of a line is just a <u>measure of the slope</u> — the steeper the line, the larger the gradient.

Q1 Work out the gradient of:

a) line A

b) line B

c) line C

d) line D

e) line E

f) line F

g) line G

h) line H

i) line I

j) line J

k) a line parallel to A

l) a line parallel to B

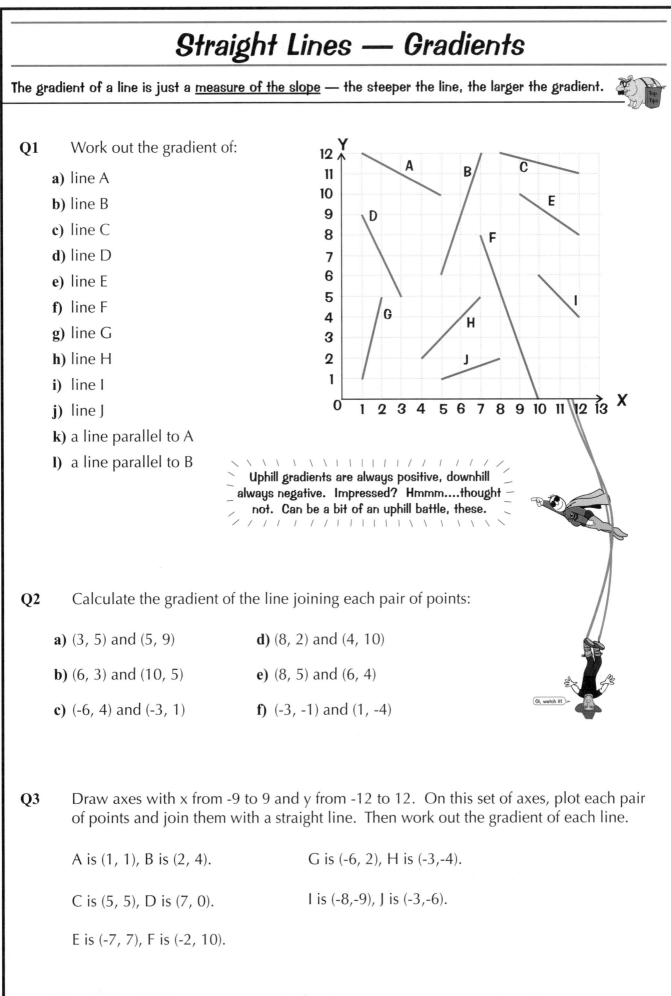

Uphill gradients are always positive, downhill always negative. Impressed? Hmmm....thought not. Can be a bit of an uphill battle, these.

Oi, watch it!

Q2 Calculate the gradient of the line joining each pair of points:

a) (3, 5) and (5, 9)

b) (6, 3) and (10, 5)

c) (-6, 4) and (-3, 1)

d) (8, 2) and (4, 10)

e) (8, 5) and (6, 4)

f) (-3, -1) and (1, -4)

Q3 Draw axes with x from -9 to 9 and y from -12 to 12. On this set of axes, plot each pair of points and join them with a straight line. Then work out the gradient of each line.

A is (1, 1), B is (2, 4).

C is (5, 5), D is (7, 0).

E is (-7, 7), F is (-2, 10).

G is (-6, 2), H is (-3,-4).

I is (-8,-9), J is (-3,-6).

More Graphs

Q1 Here are some equations, and there are some curves below.
Match the equations to the curves shown below.

a) $y = x^3 + 3$

d) $y = -x^3 + 3$

g) $y = \dfrac{2}{x}$

b) $y = 2x^3 - 3$

e) $y = x^3$

h) $y = \dfrac{1}{x^2}$

c) $y = -\dfrac{1}{2}x^3 + 2$

f) $y = -\dfrac{3}{x}$

i) $y = -\dfrac{1}{x^2}$

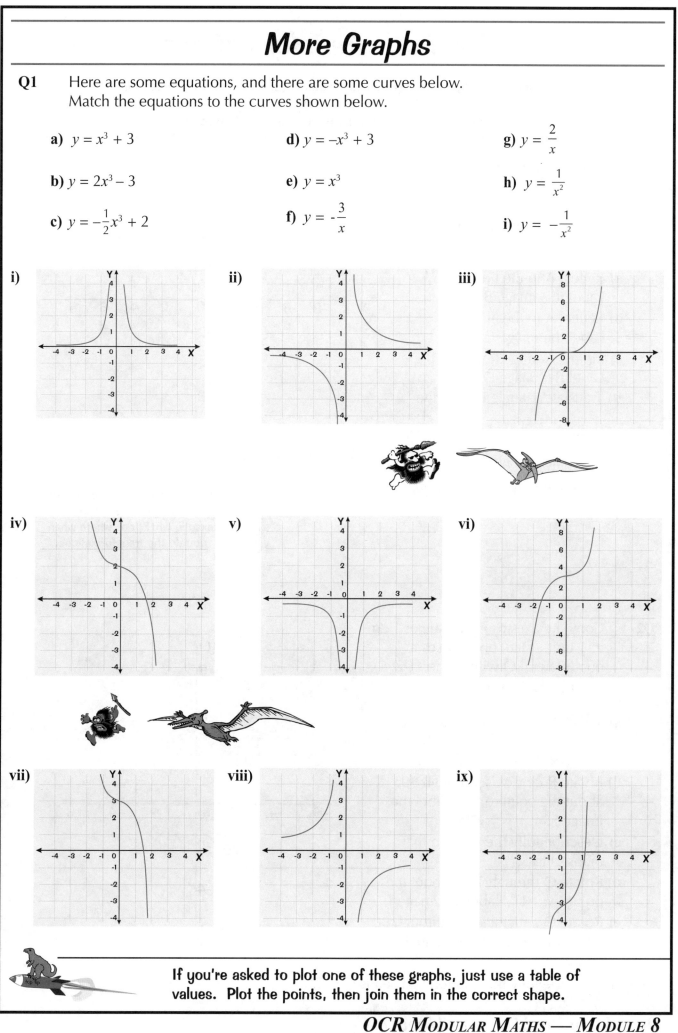

If you're asked to plot one of these graphs, just use a table of values. Plot the points, then join them in the correct shape.

The Four Transformations

Remember that good old **TERRY** is always around to help if you need him —
Translation **E**nlargement **R**otation **R**eflection, err.. **Y**ay! Make sure you can do the
transformations questions in module 6 (p.17 and 18) before you try these ones.

Q1 Copy the axes and mark on triangle A
with corners (-1, 2), (0, 4) and (-2, 4).

Use a scale of 1 cm to 1 unit.

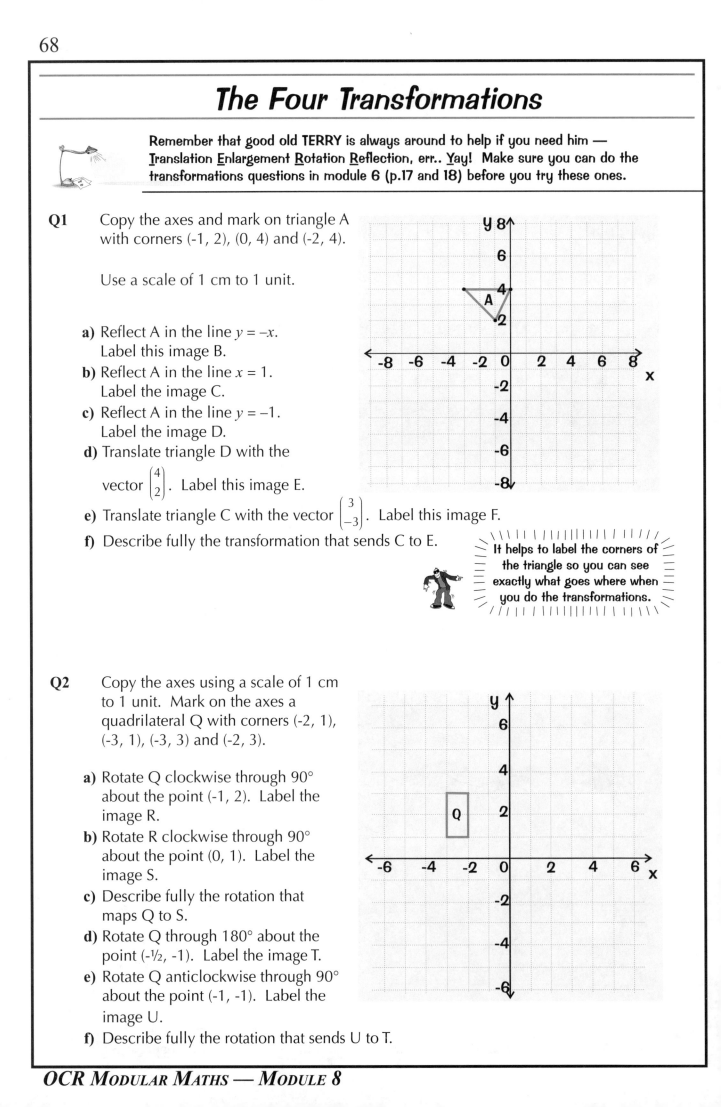

a) Reflect A in the line $y = -x$.
Label this image B.

b) Reflect A in the line $x = 1$.
Label the image C.

c) Reflect A in the line $y = -1$.
Label the image D.

d) Translate triangle D with the
vector $\begin{pmatrix} 4 \\ 2 \end{pmatrix}$. Label this image E.

e) Translate triangle C with the vector $\begin{pmatrix} 3 \\ -3 \end{pmatrix}$. Label this image F.

f) Describe fully the transformation that sends C to E.

It helps to label the corners of
the triangle so you can see
exactly what goes where when
you do the transformations.

Q2 Copy the axes using a scale of 1 cm
to 1 unit. Mark on the axes a
quadrilateral Q with corners (-2, 1),
(-3, 1), (-3, 3) and (-2, 3).

a) Rotate Q clockwise through 90°
about the point (-1, 2). Label the
image R.

b) Rotate R clockwise through 90°
about the point (0, 1). Label the
image S.

c) Describe fully the rotation that
maps Q to S.

d) Rotate Q through 180° about the
point (-½, -1). Label the image T.

e) Rotate Q anticlockwise through 90°
about the point (-1, -1). Label the
image U.

f) Describe fully the rotation that sends U to T.

The Four Transformations

Move each point separately — then check your shape hasn't
done anything unexpected while you weren't looking.

Q3 Copy the axes below using a scale of 1 cm to 1 unit.

A parallelogram A has
vertices at (6, 4), (10, 4),
(8, 10) and (12, 10).
Draw this parallelogram
onto your axes. An
enlargement scale factor
½ and centre (0, 0)
transforms
parallelogram A onto its
image B.

a) Draw this image B on
your axes.

b) Translate B by the vector
$\binom{-3}{-2}$ and label this
image C.

c) Calculate the ratio of the area of parallelogram C to the area of parallelogram A.

Q4 A is the point (4, 3), B is (4, 1) and
C is (5, 1).

a) Using a scale of 1 cm to 1 unit draw
the axes and mark on it the figure
given by ABC.

b) Reflect ABC in the x-axis and label
the image $A_1B_1C_1$.

c) Reflect $A_1B_1C_1$ in the y-axis and
label the image $A_2B_2C_2$.

d) Describe fully the single
transformation which would map
ABC onto $A_2B_2C_2$.

Q5 Draw axes with x and y running from 0 to 12 with a scale of 1 cm to 1 unit.

O is the origin. $\overrightarrow{OP} = \binom{4}{2}$, $\overrightarrow{PQ} = \binom{-1}{2}$, and $\overrightarrow{QR} = 2\overrightarrow{OP}$.

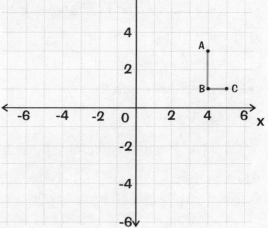

Urghh — vectors...
Make sure you get the
coordinates the right way
round — top for x dirⁿ,
bottom for y dirⁿ.

a) Mark P, Q and R on your axes.

b) Translate R by $\overrightarrow{QO}$. Label the image T.

c) Verify that $\overrightarrow{PQ} + \overrightarrow{QR} + \overrightarrow{RT} + \overrightarrow{TP} = O$.

Similarity and Enlargement

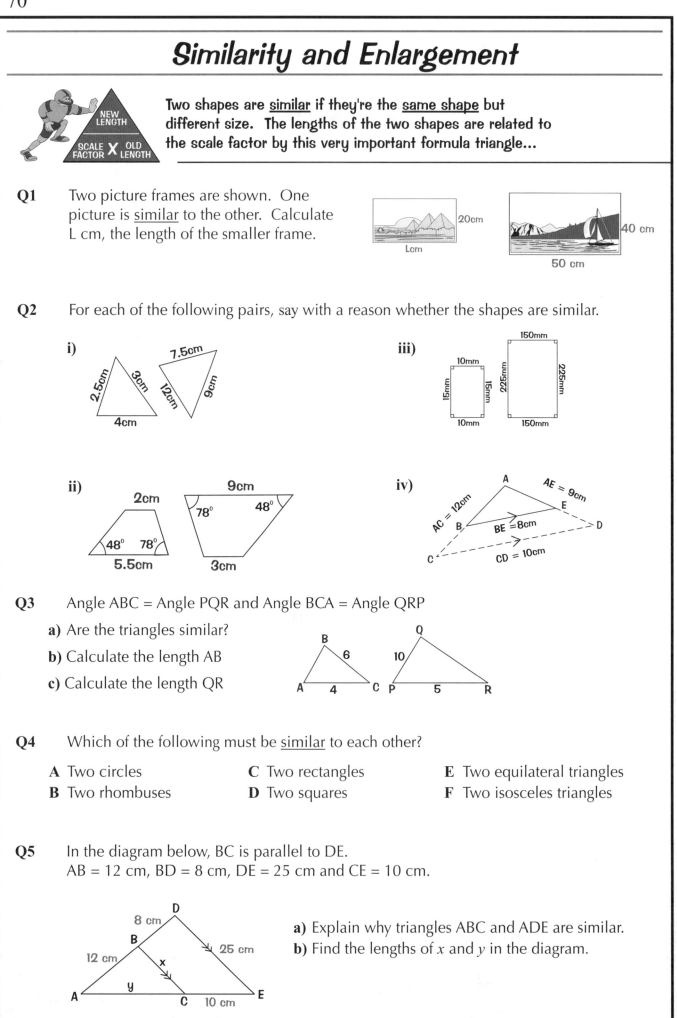

Two shapes are <u>similar</u> if they're the <u>same shape</u> but different size. The lengths of the two shapes are related to the scale factor by this very important formula triangle...

Q1 Two picture frames are shown. One picture is <u>similar</u> to the other. Calculate L cm, the length of the smaller frame.

Q2 For each of the following pairs, say with a reason whether the shapes are similar.

i)

iii)

ii)

iv)

Q3 Angle ABC = Angle PQR and Angle BCA = Angle QRP

a) Are the triangles similar?

b) Calculate the length AB

c) Calculate the length QR

Q4 Which of the following must be <u>similar</u> to each other?

A Two circles   **C** Two rectangles   **E** Two equilateral triangles
B Two rhombuses   **D** Two squares   **F** Two isosceles triangles

Q5 In the diagram below, BC is parallel to DE.
AB = 12 cm, BD = 8 cm, DE = 25 cm and CE = 10 cm.

a) Explain why triangles ABC and ADE are similar.

b) Find the lengths of x and y in the diagram.

Similarity and Enlargement

For questions 6, 7 and 8 copy out the grid and shapes onto squared paper.

Q6 Enlarge square S by a scale factor of 4. The centre of enlargement is (1, 10). Label the new square K' L' M' N'. What are the <u>coordinates</u> of these new points?

Q7 Enlarge rectangle Z by a scale factor of −3 using any method. The centre of enlargement is (13, 11).
   a) Draw the new rectangle W'X'Y'V'.
   b) What are the <u>coordinates</u> of these new points?
   c) Why doesn't an enlargement of scale factor 3 from centre (17.5, 11) produce the same result?

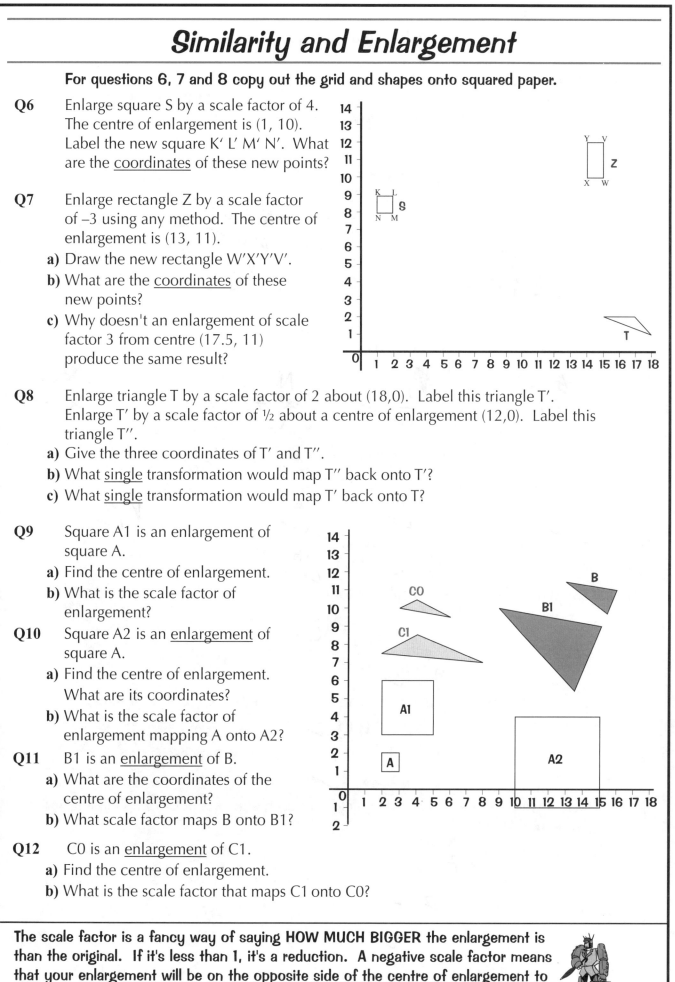

Q8 Enlarge triangle T by a scale factor of 2 about (18,0). Label this triangle T'. Enlarge T' by a scale factor of ½ about a centre of enlargement (12,0). Label this triangle T''.
   a) Give the three coordinates of T' and T''.
   b) What <u>single</u> transformation would map T'' back onto T'?
   c) What <u>single</u> transformation would map T' back onto T?

Q9 Square A1 is an enlargement of square A.
   a) Find the centre of enlargement.
   b) What is the scale factor of enlargement?

Q10 Square A2 is an <u>enlargement</u> of square A.
   a) Find the centre of enlargement. What are its coordinates?
   b) What is the scale factor of enlargement mapping A onto A2?

Q11 B1 is an <u>enlargement</u> of B.
   a) What are the coordinates of the centre of enlargement?
   b) What scale factor maps B onto B1?

Q12 C0 is an <u>enlargement</u> of C1.
   a) Find the centre of enlargement.
   b) What is the scale factor that maps C1 onto C0?

The scale factor is a fancy way of saying **HOW MUCH BIGGER** the enlargement is than the original. If it's less than 1, it's a reduction. A negative scale factor means that your enlargement will be on the opposite side of the centre of enlargement to the original shape. Look back at mod 6 p.17 for more enlargement questions.

72

Length, Area and Volume

Q1 p, q and r are lengths. State for each of the following whether the formula gives a
<u>length</u>, an <u>area</u>, a <u>volume</u> or <u>none of these</u>:

a) $p + q$ L

b) $pq - rq$ A N

c) $p^2q^2 + pr^2$ N

d) pr/q L

e) $5pqr/10$ V

f) $\pi pqr/2$ V

g) $p^3 + q^3 + r^3$ V

h) $9pr^2 - 2q$ N

Just a quick reminder: π has no units, so should just be treated as a number

Q2 w, x, y and z are lengths. State for each of the following whether the formula gives a
<u>length</u>, an <u>area</u> or a <u>volume</u>, when numbers are substituted in for the variables:

a) $\dfrac{xy}{w}$ L

b) $\dfrac{xy^2 - w^2y}{z^2}$ L

c) $\dfrac{x^3}{y} - 14wz$ N A

d) $\dfrac{x^2}{w} + \dfrac{w^2}{y} + \dfrac{y^2}{z} + \dfrac{z^3}{x^2}$ L L L L X

Q3 a, b, and c are lengths, r is the radius, $\pi = 3.14$.
State whether each of the following formulas give a <u>perimeter</u>, <u>area</u> or <u>neither</u> of these.

a) $3\pi r^2 + abc$ N

b) $6\pi r + a - 6c$ P

c) $17ab + \pi r^2$ A

d) $\dfrac{16abc}{8b}$ A

Q4 If r is a length, is $\dfrac{4}{3}\pi r^2$ a volume formula?   no

Remember — if r is a length, then r^2 is an area and r^3 is a volume.

Q5 If b and h are lengths, is ½bh an area formula?   yes

Q6 Is $\dfrac{h}{2}(x+y)$ an area formula if x, y and h are lengths?   yes

Q7 If x and h are lengths, could this be a perimeter formula: $x + x + h + h + h$?   yes

Q8 Could ½Dd be a volume formula, given that D and d are lengths?   no

Q9 The following statements are <u>incomplete</u>. For each one, find out what is missing and
rewrite the formula correctly:

a) Volume of a cube = l^3 (where l is the length)

b) Area of a circle = $\left(\pi\dfrac{d}{2}\right)^2$ (where d is the diameter)

c) Perimeter of a circle = $\pi 2r$ (where r is the radius)

Trigonometry

Before you start a trigonometry question, write down the ratios, using
SOH CAH TOA (<u>Sockatoa</u>!) — it'll help you pick your formula.

Give all your answers to 3 s.f. for these pages.

Q1 Calculate the tan, sin and cos of each of these angles:
a) 17° **b)** 83° **c)** 5° **d)** 28° **e)** 45°.

Q2 Use the tangent ratio to find the unknowns:

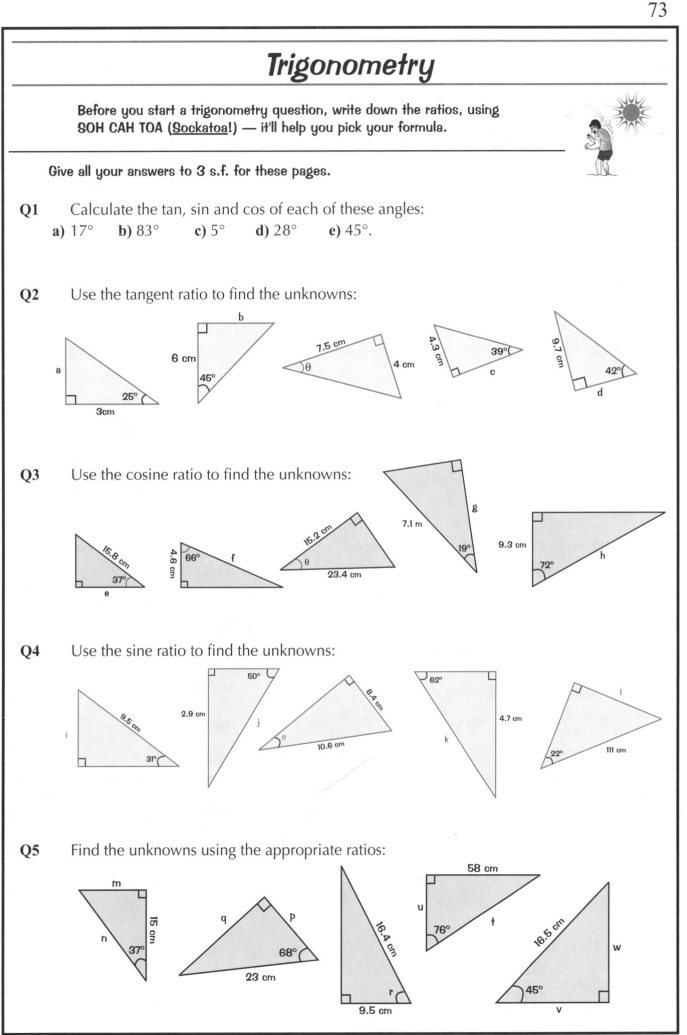

Q3 Use the cosine ratio to find the unknowns:

Q4 Use the sine ratio to find the unknowns:

Q5 Find the unknowns using the appropriate ratios:

Trigonometry

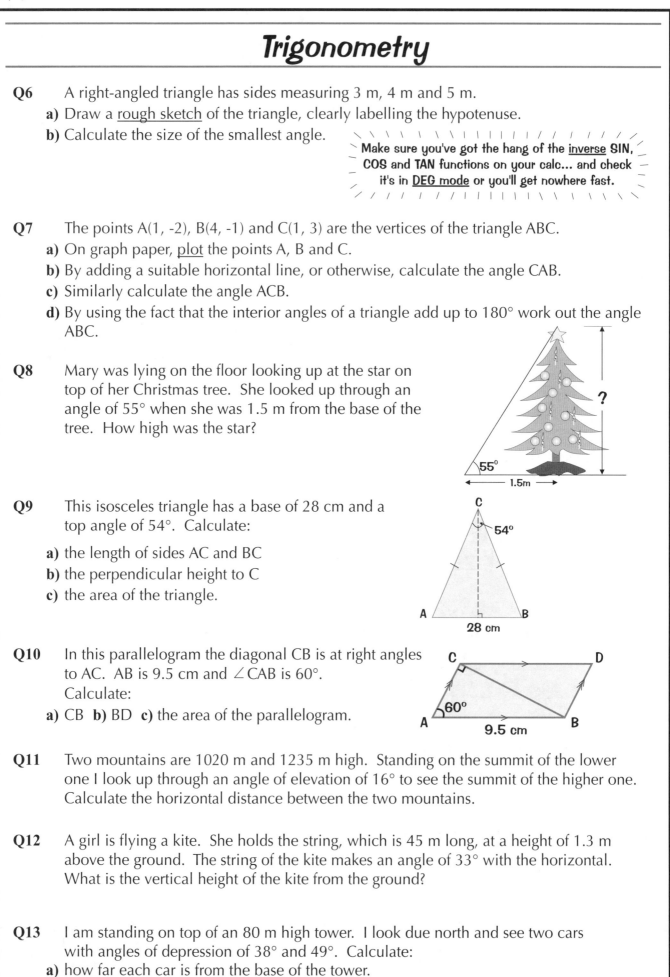

Q6 A right-angled triangle has sides measuring 3 m, 4 m and 5 m.
  a) Draw a <u>rough sketch</u> of the triangle, clearly labelling the hypotenuse.
  b) Calculate the size of the smallest angle.

> Make sure you've got the hang of the <u>inverse</u> SIN, COS and TAN functions on your calc... and check it's in <u>DEG mode</u> or you'll get nowhere fast.

Q7 The points A(1, -2), B(4, -1) and C(1, 3) are the vertices of the triangle ABC.
  a) On graph paper, <u>plot</u> the points A, B and C.
  b) By adding a suitable horizontal line, or otherwise, calculate the angle CAB.
  c) Similarly calculate the angle ACB.
  d) By using the fact that the interior angles of a triangle add up to 180° work out the angle ABC.

Q8 Mary was lying on the floor looking up at the star on top of her Christmas tree. She looked up through an angle of 55° when she was 1.5 m from the base of the tree. How high was the star?

Q9 This isosceles triangle has a base of 28 cm and a top angle of 54°. Calculate:

  a) the length of sides AC and BC
  b) the perpendicular height to C
  c) the area of the triangle.

Q10 In this parallelogram the diagonal CB is at right angles to AC. AB is 9.5 cm and ∠CAB is 60°. Calculate:
  a) CB **b)** BD **c)** the area of the parallelogram.

Q11 Two mountains are 1020 m and 1235 m high. Standing on the summit of the lower one I look up through an angle of elevation of 16° to see the summit of the higher one. Calculate the horizontal distance between the two mountains.

Q12 A girl is flying a kite. She holds the string, which is 45 m long, at a height of 1.3 m above the ground. The string of the kite makes an angle of 33° with the horizontal. What is the vertical height of the kite from the ground?

Q13 I am standing on top of an 80 m high tower. I look due north and see two cars with angles of depression of 38° and 49°. Calculate:
  a) how far each car is from the base of the tower.
  b) how far apart the cars are.

Trigonometry and Bearings

Don't try and do it all in your head — you've got to label the
sides or you're bound to mess it up. Go on, get your pen out...
Same goes for questions which don't provide a helpful diagram.
Draw one and it makes the question ten times easier!

Q1 Find the bearings required in these diagrams.

It's easy to get lost if you don't
follow the easy rule: always measure
bearings from the <u>north line</u>.

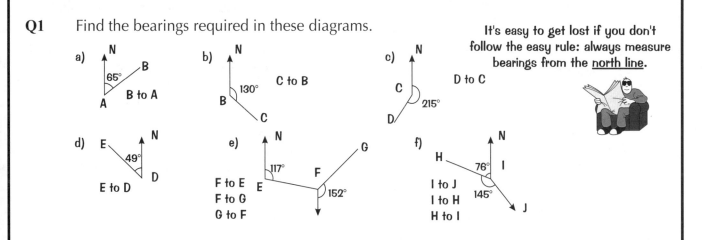

Q2 A fishing boat travels at 12 km/h for an hour due north.
It then turns due west and travels at 7 km/h for an hour.
  a) How far is it from its starting point now?
  b) What bearing must it travel on to return to base?

Q3 A plane takes off and flies due east for 153 km then turns and flies due north for 116 km.
  a) How far is it now from where it started?
  b) What is the bearing of the plane from the runway it took off from.
     The plane turns again and flies 52km on a bearing of 270°.
  c) What bearing must the plane take in order to return to the runway?

Q4 A boat travels 9 km due south and then 7 km due east.
What bearing must it travel on to return to base?

Q5 A ship sails on a bearing of 300° for 100 km. The captain can then see a lighthouse due
south of him that he knows is due west of his starting point.
Calculate how far west the lighthouse is from the ship's starting point.

I knew I should have
paid more attention
when I was at school.

OCR MODULAR MATHS — MODULE 8

Probability — Tree Diagrams

First things first — if you want some practice at calculating simple probabilities have a look back at pages 19 and 50. Calculating combined probabilities can lead to all kinds of confusion. But by drawing a tree diagram, you can make any question just about bearable.

Q1 Write independent or dependent for each pair of events:
  a) It raining today and picking a diamond from a pack of cards.
  b) Picking an ace of clubs from a pack of cards and missing the bus to work.
  c) Picking an ace from a pack of cards and keeping it, then picking another ace from the pack.
  d) Choosing a red ball from a bag, then a black ball, without replacement.

> Before you fill in any tree diagram, you need to decide whether the events are:
> 1) **Independent** — the probabilities of each event always remain the same.
> 2) **Dependent** — the probabilities change depending on what happens on the previous branch.

Q2 3 balls are drawn at random, without replacement, from a bag containing 4 green balls and 3 red balls.
  a) Copy and complete the tree diagram below showing all the possible outcomes and their probabilities.

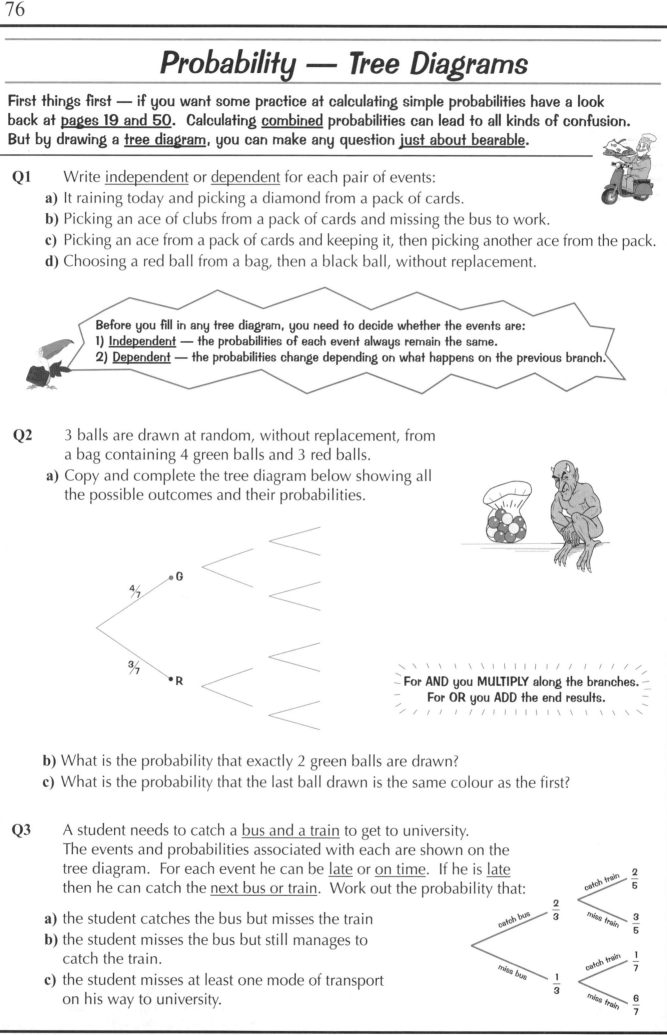

> For **AND** you **MULTIPLY** along the branches.
> For **OR** you **ADD** the end results.

  b) What is the probability that exactly 2 green balls are drawn?
  c) What is the probability that the last ball drawn is the same colour as the first?

Q3 A student needs to catch a bus and a train to get to university. The events and probabilities associated with each are shown on the tree diagram. For each event he can be late or on time. If he is late then he can catch the next bus or train. Work out the probability that:

  a) the student catches the bus but misses the train
  b) the student misses the bus but still manages to catch the train.
  c) the student misses at least one mode of transport on his way to university.

catch bus $\frac{2}{3}$ catch train $\frac{2}{5}$ miss train $\frac{3}{5}$
miss bus $\frac{1}{3}$ catch train $\frac{1}{7}$ miss train $\frac{6}{7}$

Probability — Tree Diagrams

Q4 The probability that a football team will win a match is 50%. By drawing a tree diagram, work out the chances of the team winning four games in a row.

Q5 An unbiased dice in the shape of a tetrahedron has vertices numbered 1, 2, 3, 4.
To win a game with this dice, you must throw a 4.
At each go you have a maximum of 3 attempts.

a) Using a tree diagram, calculate the probability of winning with the second throw of the first go.
b) What is the probability of winning on the first go?

Q6 3 coins are drawn at random, without replacement, from a piggy bank containing 7 pound coins and 4 twenty-pence pieces.

a) Draw a tree diagram showing all possible outcomes and their probabilities.
b) Find the probability that the first coin selected is different in value from the third.
c) Find the probability that less than £1.50 is drawn altogether.

Q7 An insurance company has 8 women and 14 men who are directors. From these directors a Chairperson and then a Personal Assistant are chosen at random by drawing names out of a hat. One person <u>cannot</u> be chosen for <u>both</u> positions.

a) What is the probability that a particular woman, Ruth, is chosen as the Chairperson?

b) Copy and complete the tree diagram. Place in the brackets the probability associated with that particular stage.

c) An extra regulation is issued by the board of directors. This states that the Chairperson and Personal Assistant must be of opposite sexes. What are the chances of this happening without having to conduct the selection process a second time?

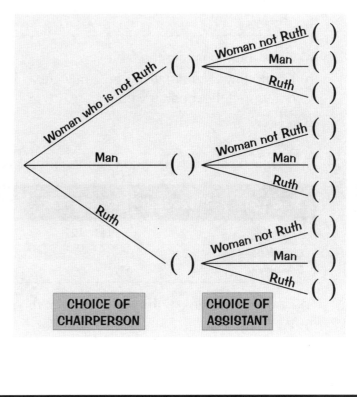

Cumulative Frequency

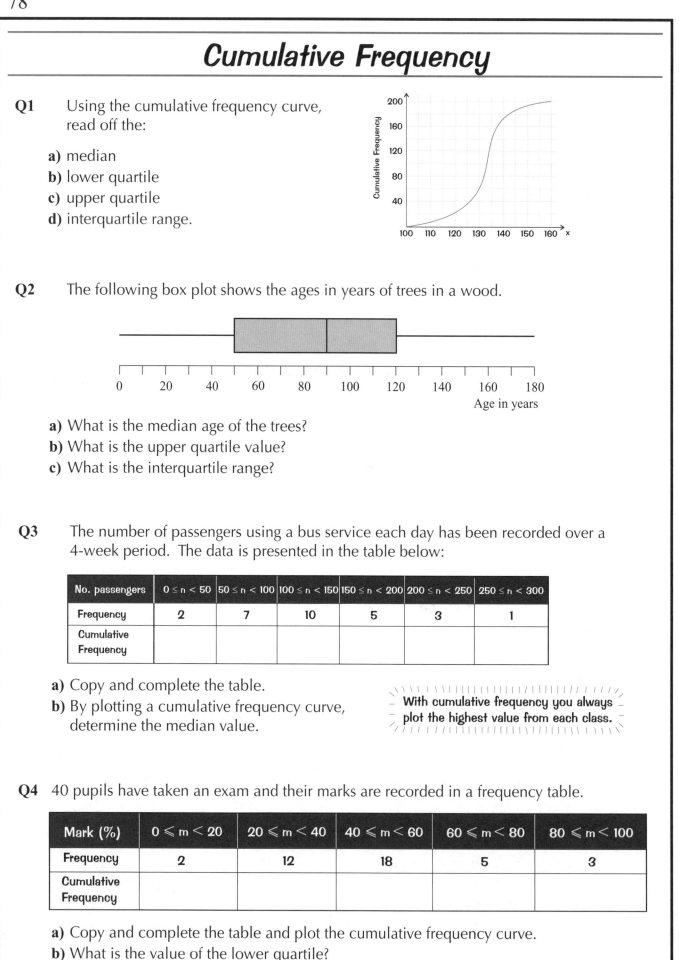

Q1 Using the cumulative frequency curve, read off the:

a) median
b) lower quartile
c) upper quartile
d) interquartile range.

Q2 The following box plot shows the ages in years of trees in a wood.

a) What is the median age of the trees?
b) What is the upper quartile value?
c) What is the interquartile range?

Q3 The number of passengers using a bus service each day has been recorded over a 4-week period. The data is presented in the table below:

No. passengers	$0 \leq n < 50$	$50 \leq n < 100$	$100 \leq n < 150$	$150 \leq n < 200$	$200 \leq n < 250$	$250 \leq n < 300$
Frequency	2	7	10	5	3	1
Cumulative Frequency						

a) Copy and complete the table.
b) By plotting a cumulative frequency curve, determine the median value.

With cumulative frequency you always plot the highest value from each class.

Q4 40 pupils have taken an exam and their marks are recorded in a frequency table.

Mark (%)	$0 \leq m < 20$	$20 \leq m < 40$	$40 \leq m < 60$	$60 \leq m < 80$	$80 \leq m < 100$
Frequency	2	12	18	5	3
Cumulative Frequency					

a) Copy and complete the table and plot the cumulative frequency curve.
b) What is the value of the lower quartile?
c) What is the interquartile range?
d) What is the median mark?

Cumulative Frequency

Q5   One hundred scores for a board game are presented in the table below.
Copy and complete the table.

Score	$31 \leq s < 41$	$41 \leq s < 51$	$51 \leq s < 61$	$61 \leq s < 71$	$71 \leq s < 81$	$81 \leq s < 91$	$91 \leq s < 101$
Frequency	4	12	21	32	19	8	4
Cumulative Frequency							

a) Which group contains the median score?
b) By plotting the cumulative frequency curve determine the actual value of the median score.
c) Find the interquartile range.

Q6   The following frequency table gives the distribution of the lives of electric bulbs.

a) Copy and complete the frequency table.

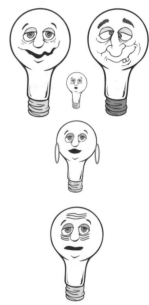

Life (hours)	Frequency	Cumulative Frequency
$900 \leq L < 1000$	10	
$1000 \leq L < 1100$	12	
$1100 \leq L < 1200$	15	
$1200 \leq L < 1300$	18	
$1300 \leq L < 1400$	22	
$1400 \leq L < 1500$	17	
$1500 \leq L < 1600$	14	
$1600 \leq L < 1700$	9	

b) Which group contains the median value?
c) By drawing the cumulative frequency curve, find the actual value of the median.
d) Determine values for the upper and lower quartiles.

Q7   30 pupils recorded the time taken (minutes : seconds) to boil some water.
Here are their results: 2:37 2:37 3:17 3:30 2:45 2:13 3:18 3:12 3:38 3:29
3:04 3:24 4:13 3:01 3:11 2:33 3:37 4:24 3:59 3:11
3:22 3:13 2:57 3:12 3:07 4:17 3:31 3:42 3:51 3:24

a) By using a tally, transfer the data into a copy of the frequency table. Complete the table.

Time	$2:00 \leqslant t < 2:30$	$2:30 \leqslant t < 3:00$	$3:00 \leqslant t < 3:30$	$3:30 \leqslant t < 4:00$	$4:00 \leqslant t < 4:30$
Tally					
Frequency					
Cumulative Frequency					

b) Draw the cumulative frequency curve.
c) Using your graph, read off the median and the upper and lower quartiles.
d) What is the interquartile range?

Spread of Data

The shapes of graphs are very important — if you want to talk about the spread of data that is. Make sure you know what the shapes of histograms and cumulative frequency curves tell you about a set of data.

Q1 Below are two histograms — one shows the weights of a sample of 16 year olds, and the other shows the weights of a sample of 1 kg bags of sugar. Say which is which.

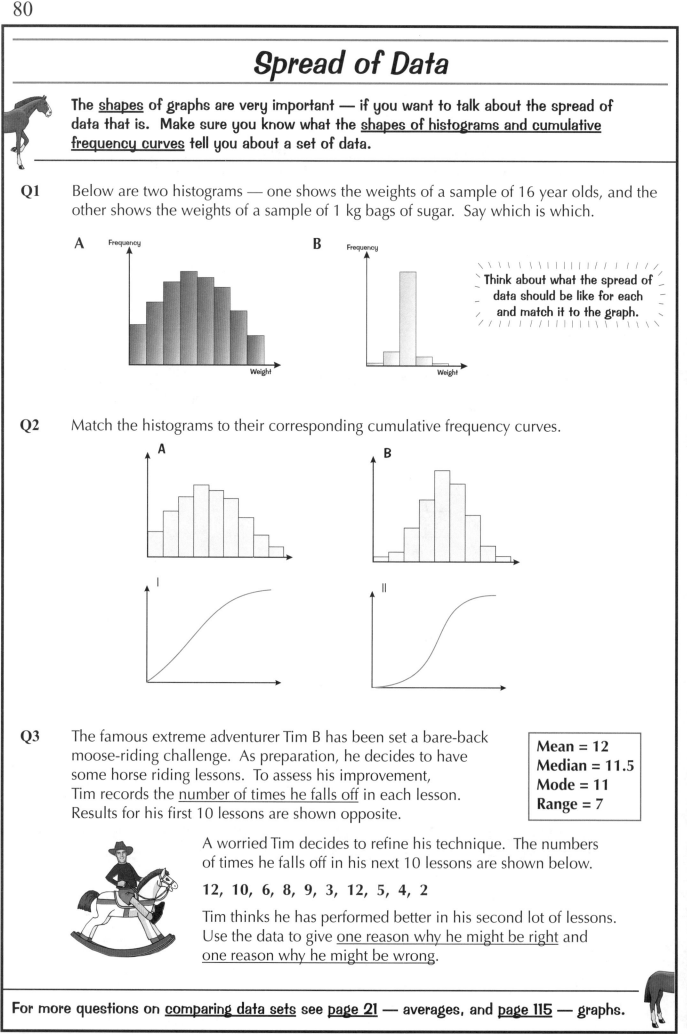

Think about what the spread of data should be like for each and match it to the graph.

Q2 Match the histograms to their corresponding cumulative frequency curves.

Q3 The famous extreme adventurer Tim B has been set a bare-back moose-riding challenge. As preparation, he decides to have some horse riding lessons. To assess his improvement, Tim records the number of times he falls off in each lesson. Results for his first 10 lessons are shown opposite.

Mean = 12
Median = 11.5
Mode = 11
Range = 7

A worried Tim decides to refine his technique. The numbers of times he falls off in his next 10 lessons are shown below.

12, 10, 6, 8, 9, 3, 12, 5, 4, 2

Tim thinks he has performed better in his second lot of lessons. Use the data to give one reason why he might be right and one reason why he might be wrong.

For more questions on comparing data sets see page 21 — averages, and page 115 — graphs.

OCR Modular Maths — Module 8

Calculation Bounds

To find the upper or lower bound of a calculation, you've just got to decide which version of the values involved (max or min) to use to get the biggest or smallest overall answer.

Q1 Jodie weighs herself on some scales that are accurate to the nearest 10 grams. The digital display shows her weight as 64.78 kg.
   a) What is the maximum that she could weigh?
   b) What is the minimum that she could weigh?

Q2 A rectangular rug is 1.8 metres long and 0.7 metres wide. Both measurements are given correct to one decimal place.
   a) State the minimum possible length of the rug.
   b) Calculate the maximum possible area of the rug.

Q3 $R = \dfrac{S}{T}$ is a formula used by stockbrokers.

   S = 940, correct to 2 significant figures and T = 5.56, correct to 3 significant figures.

   a) For the value of S, write down the upper bound and the lower bound.
   b) For the value of T, write down the upper bound and the lower bound.
   c) Calculate the upper bound and lower bound for R.
   d) Write down the value of R correct to an appropriate number of significant figures.

> Remember — you don't always get the maximum value by using the biggest input values.

Q4 A = 13, correct to 2 significant figures.
   B = 12.5, correct to 3 significant figures.
   a) For the value of A, write down the upper bound and the lower bound.
   b) For the value of B, write down the upper bound and the lower bound.
   c) Calculate the upper bound and lower bound for C when C = AB.

Q5 A lorry travelled 125 kilometres in 1 hour and 50 minutes. If the time was measured to the nearest 10 minutes and the distance to the nearest five kilometres, what was the maximum value of the average speed of the lorry, in kilometres per hour?

Q6 Whilst being chased by a man-eating rodent, Tim B the famous extreme-adventurer runs a distance of 100 m in 12.3 seconds.

If this time is accurate to the nearest 0.1 seconds and the distance to the nearest metre, what is the maximum value of his average speed, in metres per second?

Powers and Standard Form

Powers questions are great fun once you've learned the <u>magical power laws</u>. Without them you'll be as clueless as Mr Clueless from planet Clueless trying to hitchhike to Clueville.

No calculators for this page, by the way.

Q1 Which of the following are <u>true</u>?

a) $2^{-3} = 1/6$ c) $4^{-2} = 1/16$ e) $1/9 = 3^2$

b) $17^0 = 0$ d) $1^{-17} = 1$ f) $28^0 = 1$

Q2 Write the following as a single power:

a) $6^3 \times 6^5 \times 6^{-4}$ e) $16^3 \times 4^{-3} \div 4^4$

b) $(6^3)^2$ f) $(3^2)^4 \div (3^3)^3$

c) $2^0 \times 2^{-3} \times 4^2$ g) $(25^1)^3 \div (5^3)$

d) $3^4 \div 3^5 \times 3^3$ h) $2^3 \div 16^{-3}$

Some of these are pretty tricky — do them in <u>stages</u> using one power law each time.

Q3 Work out these nasty beasties.

a) 4^0 d) 10^{-3} g) $8^{-\frac{1}{3}}$ j) $3^3 \times 4^0$

b) 35^1 e) $5^2 \div 2^{-2}$ h) $125^{-\frac{1}{3}}$ k) $4^{\frac{3}{2}}$

c) 2^{-1} f) $16^{-1} \times 4^2 \times 2^4$ i) $25^{\frac{1}{2}}$ l)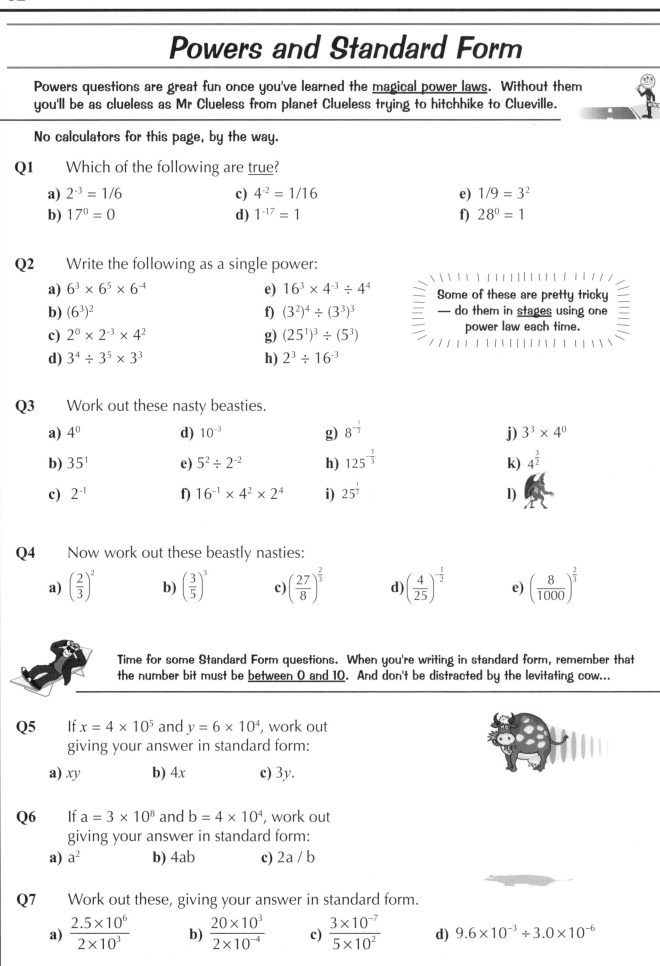

Q4 Now work out these beastly nasties:

a) $\left(\frac{2}{3}\right)^2$ b) $\left(\frac{3}{5}\right)^3$ c) $\left(\frac{27}{8}\right)^{\frac{2}{3}}$ d) $\left(\frac{4}{25}\right)^{-\frac{1}{2}}$ e) $\left(\frac{8}{1000}\right)^{\frac{2}{3}}$

Time for some Standard Form questions. When you're writing in standard form, remember that the number bit must be <u>between 0 and 10</u>. And don't be distracted by the levitating cow...

Q5 If $x = 4 \times 10^5$ and $y = 6 \times 10^4$, work out giving your answer in standard form:

a) xy b) $4x$ c) $3y$.

Q6 If $a = 3 \times 10^8$ and $b = 4 \times 10^4$, work out giving your answer in standard form:

a) a^2 b) $4ab$ c) $2a / b$

Q7 Work out these, giving your answer in standard form.

a) $\dfrac{2.5 \times 10^6}{2 \times 10^3}$ b) $\dfrac{20 \times 10^3}{2 \times 10^{-4}}$ c) $\dfrac{3 \times 10^{-7}}{5 \times 10^2}$ d) $9.6 \times 10^{-3} \div 3.0 \times 10^{-6}$

For more practice of standard form, look back at p54-55.

Basic Algebra

Before you start, look at page 57 from module 8 on expanding double brackets —
you need this for module 9 too. Good, now you're ready for this page which I'm
afraid is a rather barren expanse of algebra stretching as far as the eye can see.

Q1 Factorise each of the following:

a) $2x + 6$ f) $3y + xy$ k) $12x + 24xyz$

b) $4x + 16$ g) $3y + xy^2$ l) $5x^2 + 10x$

c) $5x + 30$ h) $4y - 8yz$ m) $7x^2 + 21x$

d) $3x - 18$ i) $6x + 12xy$ n) $16x^2 + 8x$

e) $2x + xy$ j) $10z + 20yz$ o) $18y^2 - 9y$

Q2 Factorise:

a) $7a^2bc^2 + 14ab^2c + 21ab^2c^2 + 28a^2b^2\,c^2$

b) $100x^2yz + 90x^3yz + 80x^2y^2z + 70x^2yz + 60x^2yz^2$

Q3 Simplify the following by cancelling down where possible:

a) $\dfrac{27x^4y^2z}{9x^3yz^2}$ b) $\dfrac{48a^2b^2}{(2a)^2c}$ c) $\dfrac{3xyz}{9x^2y^3z^4}$ d) $\dfrac{4p^3q^3}{(2pr)^3}$

Q4 Rearrange the following to make the letter in brackets the new subject.

a) $pq = 3p + 4r - 2q$ (p) g) $\sqrt{hk^2 - 14} = k$ (k)

b) $fg + 2e = 5 - 2g$ (g) h) $2\sqrt{x} + y = z\sqrt{x} + 4$ (x)

c) $a(b - 2) = c(b + 3)$ (b) i) $\dfrac{a}{b} = \dfrac{1}{3}(b - a)$ (a)

d) $pq^2 = rq^2 + 4$ (q) j) $\dfrac{m+n}{m-n} = \dfrac{3}{4}$ (m)

e) $4(a - b) + c(a - 2) = ad$ (a) k) $\sqrt{\dfrac{d-e}{e}} = 7$ (e)

f) $\dfrac{x^2}{3} - y = x^2$ (x) l) $\dfrac{x - 2y}{xy} = 3$ (y)

There's plenty more of these to practise on p59 plus some easier ones on p34.

These are getting quite tricky — you've got to <u>collect like</u>
<u>terms</u>, before you can make anything else the subject.

Q5 Rearrange the following formulas to make y the new subject.

a) $x(y - 1) = y$

b) $x(y + 2) = y - 3$

c) $x = \dfrac{y^2 + 1}{2y^2 - 1}$

d) $x = \dfrac{2y^2 + 1}{3y^2 - 2}$

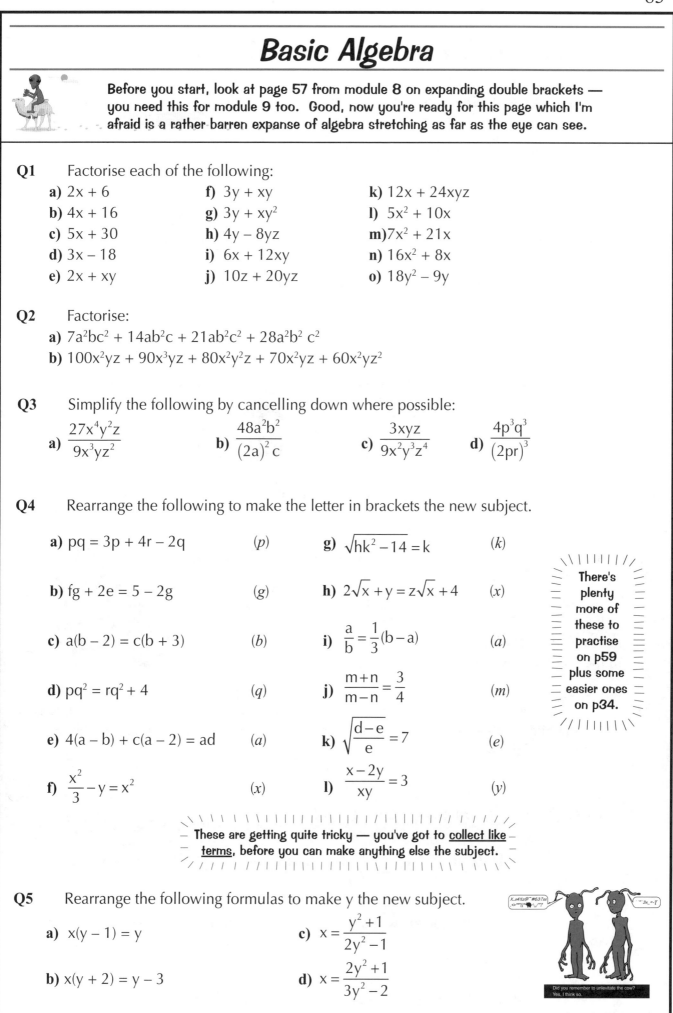

84

Direct and Inverse Proportion

Q1 If it takes 4 people 28 hours to complete a task, how long would it take just one person?

Q2 A person earns £6.20 an hour. How much do they earn for 15½ hours work?

Q3 On a map, 2 cm represents 3 km.
a) If two towns are 14 km apart, what is the distance between them on the map?
b) If two road junctions are 20.3 cm apart on the map, what is their real distance apart?

Q4 y is directly proportional to x. If $y = 5$ when x is 25, find y when x is 100.

Q5 If $y \propto x$ and $y = 132$ when $x = 10$, find the value of y when $x = 14$.

Q6 Complete the following tables of values where y is always directly proportional to x.

a)

X	2	4	6
y	5	10	

b)

X	3	6	9
y		9	

c)

X	27		
y	5	10	15

Q7 If $y = 3$ when $x = 8$ and y is inversely proportional to x, find the value of y when $x = 12$.

Q8 If $y \propto \dfrac{1}{x}$ and $x = 4$ when $y = 5$, find the value of x when $y = 10$.

Q9 If y and x vary inversely, and $y = 12$ when $x = 3$ find:
a) the value of x when $y = 9$
b) the value of y when $x = 6$.

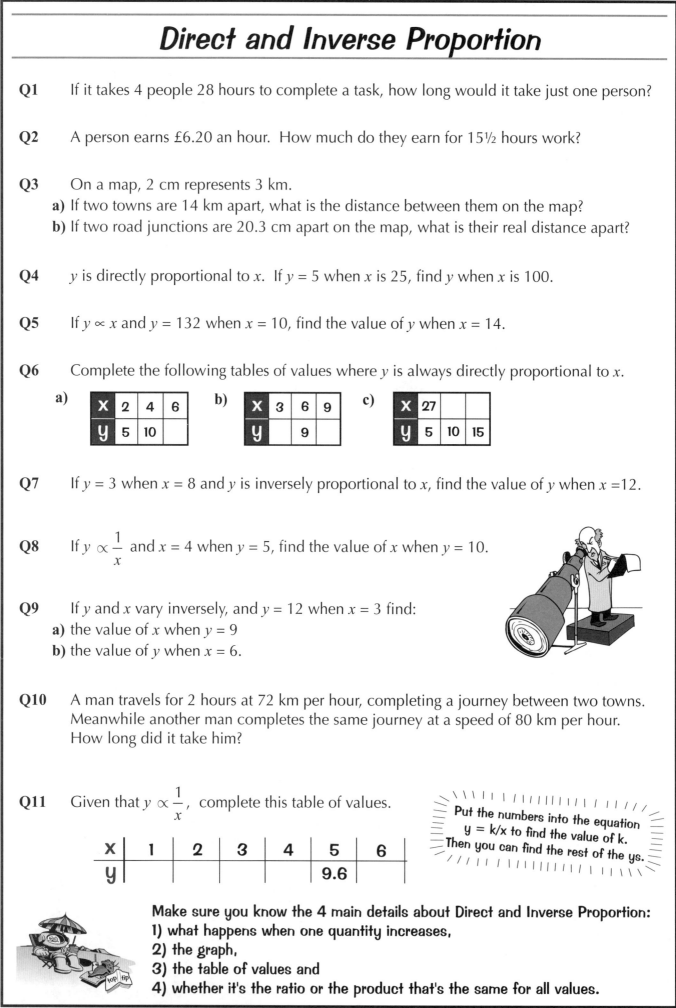

Q10 A man travels for 2 hours at 72 km per hour, completing a journey between two towns. Meanwhile another man completes the same journey at a speed of 80 km per hour. How long did it take him?

Q11 Given that $y \propto \dfrac{1}{x}$, complete this table of values.

x	1	2	3	4	5	6
y					9.6	

Put the numbers into the equation $y = k/x$ to find the value of k. Then you can find the rest of the ys.

Make sure you know the 4 main details about Direct and Inverse Proportion:
1) what happens when one quantity increases,
2) the graph,
3) the table of values and
4) whether it's the ratio or the product that's the same for all values.

Direct and Inverse Proportion

Q12 The area of a circle is proportional to the square of the radius.
If the area is 113 cm² (3 s.f.) when the radius is 6 cm, find:
a) the area of a circle with radius 5 cm
b) the radius of a circle with area 29 cm².
Give your answers to 2 s.f.

Q13 If y is inversely proportional to the square of x, and $y = 4$ when $x = 6$.
Find the value of:
a) y when $x = 3$
b) x when $y = 9$, given that x is negative.

Q14 If $y \propto x^2$ and $y = 4$ when $x = 4$, find the value of y when $x = 12$.

Q15 $y = kx^3$ and $y = 200$ when $x = 5$.
a) Find the value of k.
b) Find the value of y when $x = 8$.
c) Find the value of x when $y = 2433.4$.

Q16 Two cylindrical containers are filled
to the same depth, d cm, with water.
The mass of the water in each
container is proportional to the
square of the radius of each
container. The first container has a
radius of 16 cm and the water has a
mass of 16 kg. If the second
container has a radius of 8 cm, find
the mass of the water inside it.

d cm   r = 16 cm   d cm   r = 8 cm

Q17 Given that r varies inversely as the square of s, and $r = 24$ when $s = 10$, find the values of:
a) r when $s = 5$
b) s when $r = 150$, given that s is positive
c) r when $s = 2$
d) s when $r = 37\frac{1}{2}$, given that s is negative

> Don't forget about that little joker,
> the "inverse square" variation — they'll
> expect you to know that, too.

Q18 By considering the values in the table, decide whether $y \propto x$, $y \propto \dfrac{1}{x}$, $y \propto x^2$ or $y \propto \dfrac{1}{x^2}$.
a) Write down the equation which shows
how y varies with x.
b) Find the value of y when $x = 6.4$
c) Find the value of x when $y = 16$.

x	1.2	2.5	3.2	4.8
y	166⅔	80	62.5	41⅔

Quadratic Equations

The simplest way to solve a quadratic equation of the form "$ax^2 + bx + c = 0$" is by factorising it into two brackets. If the equation isn't in the form above, don't panic, just <u>rearrange it</u>.

Q1 Rearrange into the form "$x^2 + bx + c = 0$", then solve by factorising:

a) $x^2 + 6x = 40$

b) $x^2 + 5x = 6$

c) $x^2 + 4x = 32$

d) $x^2 = 8x$

e) $x^2 = x$

f) $x^2 - 18 = 7x$

g) $x^2 - 300 = 20x$

h) $x^2 + 48 = 26x$

i) $x^2 + 36 = 13x$

j) $x + 5 - \dfrac{14}{x} = 0$

k) $x + 4 - \dfrac{21}{x} = 0$

l) $x(x - 3) = 10$

m) $x^2 - 3(x + 6) = 0$

n) $x - \dfrac{63}{x} = 2$

o) $x + 1 = \dfrac{12}{x}$

Q2 Solving the following quadratics by factorisation.

a) $6x^2 - x - 2 = 0$

b) $4x^2 - 15x + 9 = 0$

c) $x^2 - 3x = 0$

d) $36x^2 - 48x + 16 = 0$

e) $3x^2 + 8x = 0$

f) $2x^2 - 7x - 4 = 0$

g) $4x^2 + 8x - 12 = 0$

h) $3x^2 - 11x - 20 = 0$

i) $x + 3 = 2x^2$

j) $5 - 3x - 2x^2 = 0$

k) $1 - 5x + 6x^2 = 0$

l) $3(x^2 + 2x) = 9$

m) $x^2 + 4(x - 3) = 0$

n) $x^2 = 2(4 - x)$

When "a" isn't 1, factorising gets a bit trickier. But stick with it and you'll work out the brackets eventually.

Q3 Simplify the following by cancelling down where possible:

a) $\dfrac{(x + 3)^2(x - 5)}{(x + 3)(x^2 - 25)}$

b) $\dfrac{x^2 + 13x + 42}{x + 7}$

c) $\dfrac{x^2 - 1}{(x + 1)^2}$

d) $\dfrac{x^2 - x - 12}{(3 - x)(4 - x)}$

If you're stuck, just try a little factorisation... and if that doesn't work, then try a little tenderness.

Q4 A square room has a floor of sides x metres.
The height of the walls is 3 m. Write down an expression for:

a) the floor area

b) the area of all four walls.

c) If the total area of the floor and the four walls is 64 m², form a quadratic equation and solve it to find x.

Q5 A triangle has height $(x + 1)$ cm and a base of $2x$ cm.

a) Write down an expression for the area of the triangle and simplify it.

b) If the area of the triangle is 12 cm², find the value of x.

$(x + 1)$cm

$2x$ cm

Straight Lines

Rather than jumping straight into finding the equation of a straight line, you might like some practice at finding gradients and the like. If so, have a look back at pages 64-66 for all things "straight-lines".

Q1 Find the equations of the following lines:
 a) A
 b) B
 c) C
 d) D
 e) E
 f) F

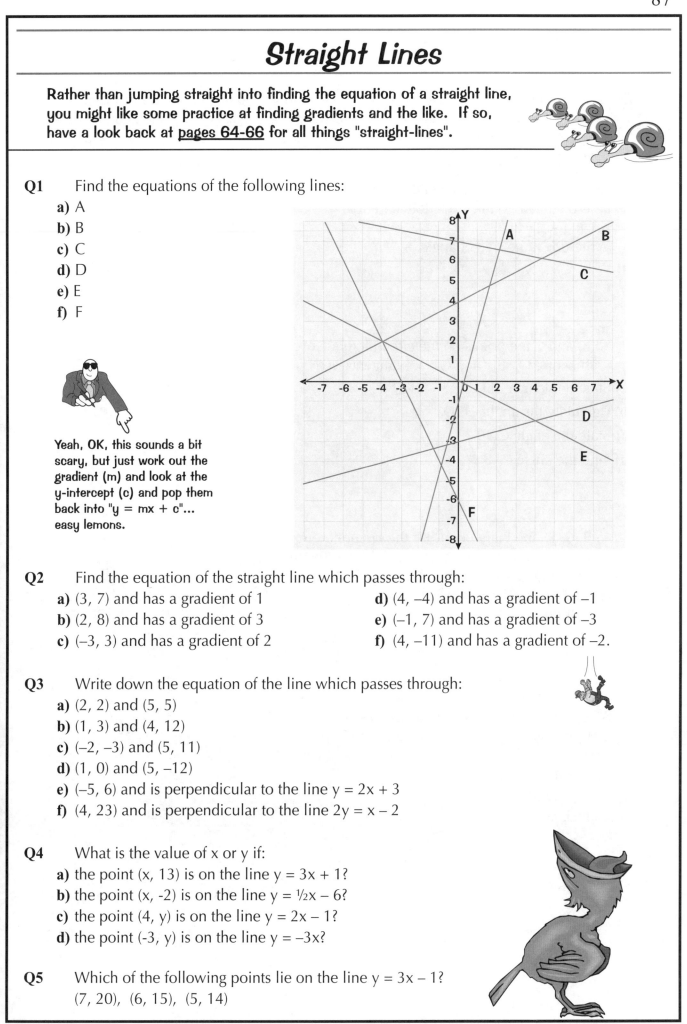

Yeah, OK, this sounds a bit scary, but just work out the gradient (m) and look at the y-intercept (c) and pop them back into "y = mx + c"... easy lemons.

Q2 Find the equation of the straight line which passes through:
 a) (3, 7) and has a gradient of 1
 b) (2, 8) and has a gradient of 3
 c) (–3, 3) and has a gradient of 2
 d) (4, –4) and has a gradient of –1
 e) (–1, 7) and has a gradient of –3
 f) (4, –11) and has a gradient of –2.

Q3 Write down the equation of the line which passes through:
 a) (2, 2) and (5, 5)
 b) (1, 3) and (4, 12)
 c) (–2, –3) and (5, 11)
 d) (1, 0) and (5, –12)
 e) (–5, 6) and is perpendicular to the line y = 2x + 3
 f) (4, 23) and is perpendicular to the line 2y = x – 2

Q4 What is the value of x or y if:
 a) the point (x, 13) is on the line y = 3x + 1?
 b) the point (x, -2) is on the line y = ½x – 6?
 c) the point (4, y) is on the line y = 2x – 1?
 d) the point (-3, y) is on the line y = –3x?

Q5 Which of the following points lie on the line y = 3x – 1?
 (7, 20), (6, 15), (5, 14)

Circle Geometry

This topic confuses me — I just seem to go round and round in circles. To avoid such confusion I recommend learning the **9 simple rules**, then you can breeze through the exam without doing the wrong thing and going off on a tangent.

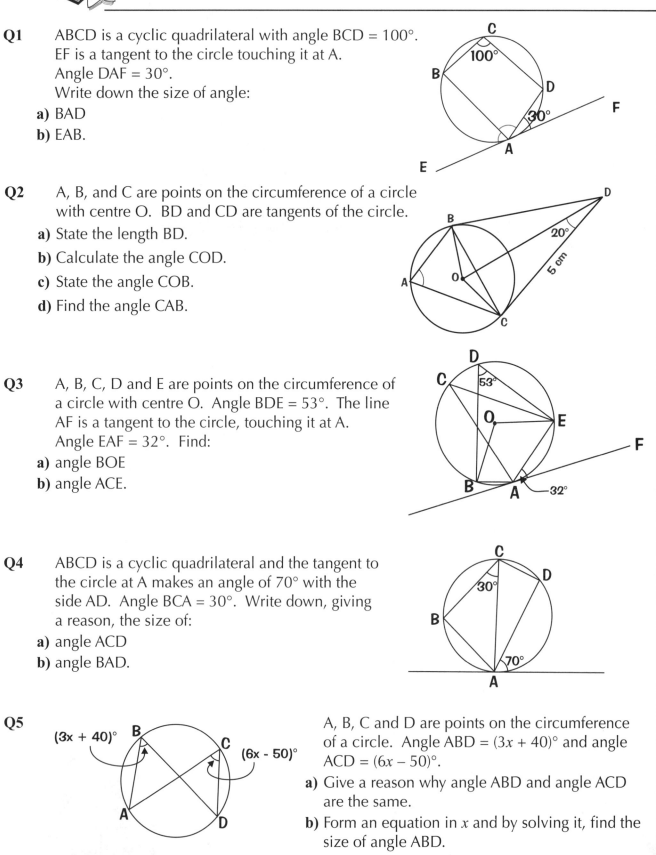

Q1 ABCD is a cyclic quadrilateral with angle BCD = 100°.
EF is a tangent to the circle touching it at A.
Angle DAF = 30°.
Write down the size of angle:
a) BAD
b) EAB.

Q2 A, B, and C are points on the circumference of a circle with centre O. BD and CD are tangents of the circle.
a) State the length BD.
b) Calculate the angle COD.
c) State the angle COB.
d) Find the angle CAB.

Q3 A, B, C, D and E are points on the circumference of a circle with centre O. Angle BDE = 53°. The line AF is a tangent to the circle, touching it at A. Angle EAF = 32°. Find:
a) angle BOE
b) angle ACE.

Q4 ABCD is a cyclic quadrilateral and the tangent to the circle at A makes an angle of 70° with the side AD. Angle BCA = 30°. Write down, giving a reason, the size of:
a) angle ACD
b) angle BAD.

Q5
$(3x + 40)°$

$(6x - 50)°$

A, B, C and D are points on the circumference of a circle. Angle ABD = $(3x + 40)°$ and angle ACD = $(6x - 50)°$.
a) Give a reason why angle ABD and angle ACD are the same.
b) Form an equation in x and by solving it, find the size of angle ABD.

Circle Geometry

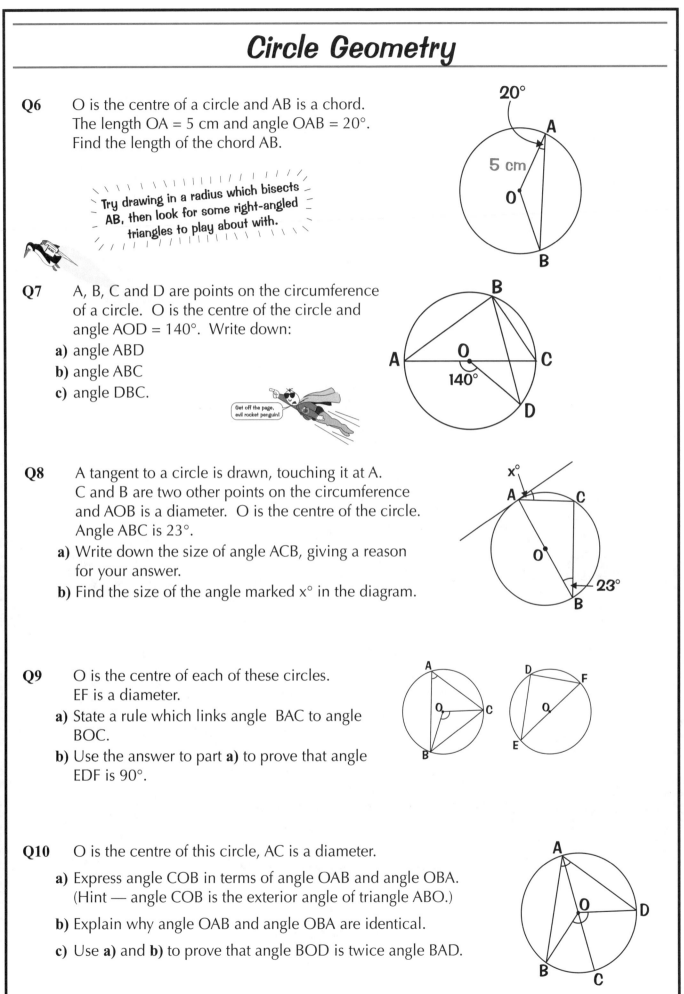

Q6 O is the centre of a circle and AB is a chord. The length OA = 5 cm and angle OAB = 20°. Find the length of the chord AB.

Try drawing in a radius which bisects AB, then look for some right-angled triangles to play about with.

Q7 A, B, C and D are points on the circumference of a circle. O is the centre of the circle and angle AOD = 140°. Write down:

a) angle ABD

b) angle ABC

c) angle DBC.

Get off the page, evil rocket penguin!

Q8 A tangent to a circle is drawn, touching it at A. C and B are two other points on the circumference and AOB is a diameter. O is the centre of the circle. Angle ABC is 23°.

a) Write down the size of angle ACB, giving a reason for your answer.

b) Find the size of the angle marked x° in the diagram.

Q9 O is the centre of each of these circles. EF is a diameter.

a) State a rule which links angle BAC to angle BOC.

b) Use the answer to part **a)** to prove that angle EDF is 90°.

Q10 O is the centre of this circle, AC is a diameter.

a) Express angle COB in terms of angle OAB and angle OBA. (Hint — angle COB is the exterior angle of triangle ABO.)

b) Explain why angle OAB and angle OBA are identical.

c) Use **a)** and **b)** to prove that angle BOD is twice angle BAD.

Area and Volume

Q1 In each of the following circles, O is the centre. Calculate the following to 3 s.f.:

a) The area of the shaded section between A and B.
b) The length of the major arc between A and B.
c) The area of the major sector between C and D.
d) The length of the minor arc between C and D.
e) The radius of the circle, if the major sector between E and F has an area of 34.2cm².
f) The length of the minor arc between E and F.

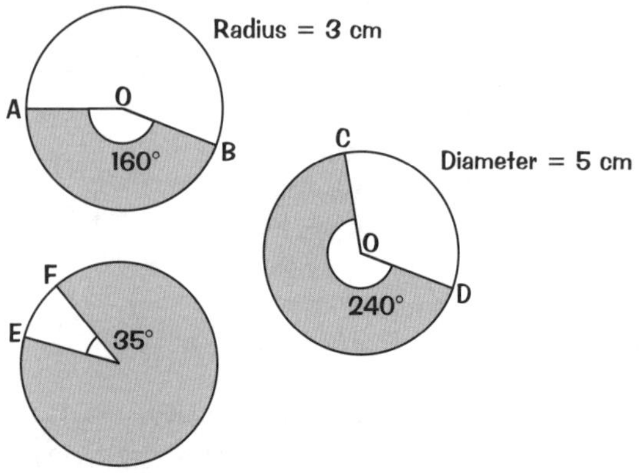

Radius = 3 cm

Diameter = 5 cm

160°

240°

35°

Q2 a) A basketball has a diameter of 24 cm. What is its volume?
b) A football has a volume of 5575 cm³. What is its radius?
c) The largest of the pyramids in Egypt is 146.6 m tall and has a square base measuring 220 m by 220 m. Calculate its volume to the nearest 100 m³.

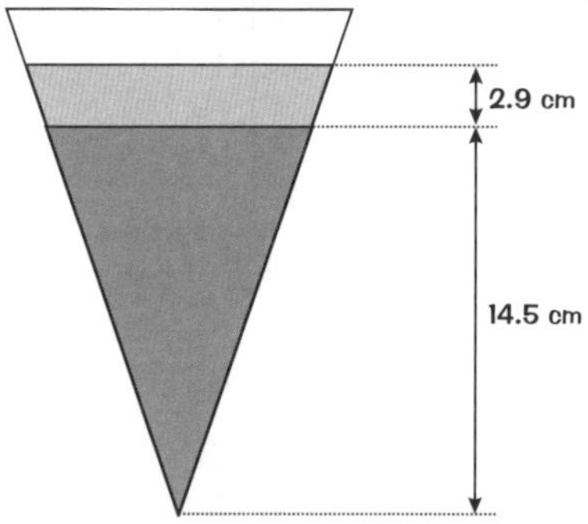

Q3 Archie the frog is investigating a cone-shaped blender. A vertical cross section of the blender is shown to the left.

2.9 cm

14.5 cm

a) The volume of water in the cone is 379.6 cm³ and the depth is 14.5 cm. Calculate the surface area of the water visible at the top of the blender.

b) Archie tries to take a drink from the blender but unfortunately topples in, increasing the level of the water by 2.9 cm. Calculate Archie's volume.

It's like a jacuzzi — with consequences.

Q4 A novelty soup can is produced. It is a hemisphere (half a sphere) joined to part of a cone.

Calculate the volume of soup which will fit into this new design of soup can.

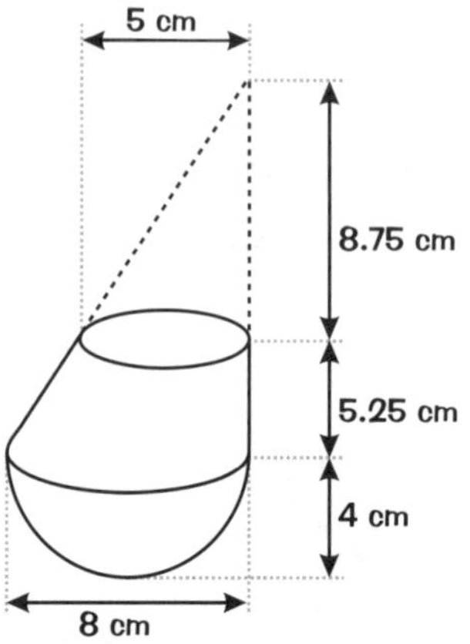

To calculate the volume of the section of cone you'll need to work out the volume of the whole cone, then the volume of the smaller cone which needs to be chopped off, and then do some subtracting.

5 cm

8.75 cm

5.25 cm

4 cm

8 cm

Area and Volume — Enlargements

Q1 Two cups A and B are similar. Cup A has a height of 15 cm and cup B has a height of 10 cm. Cup A has a volume of 54 cm³. Calculate the volume of cup B.

15 cm Brian

10 cm Max

A   **B**

Q2 Bobby the Brat has a doll which is mathematically similar to himself. He covers himself in blackcurrant squash and decides that his doll needs the same treatment. Bobby is 1.2 m tall and his doll is 60 cm tall. If it takes 2 litres of squash to cover Bobby, how much will to take to coat his doll?

> A tricky question this one. It talks about litres which makes you think of volume. However, it asks you how much is needed to <u>cover</u> Bobby's doll, not fill it, which is actually surface area!

Q3 A cylindrical bottle can hold 1 litre of oil. A second cylindrical bottle has twice the radius but the same height. It also contains oil.

a) Explain why these bottles are not similar.

b) How much oil can the larger bottle hold?

Q4 A box of chocolates is to have the shape of a cuboid 15 cm long, 8 cm wide and 10 cm high.

a) Calculate the area of material needed to make the box (assuming no flaps are required for glueing).

b) In advertising the chocolates, the manufacturer decides he will have a box made in a similar shape. The enlargement is to have a scale factor of 50. Calculate the area of material required to make the box for publicity. Give your answer in square metres.

Nettles's Chocolates

New: smoky bacon flavour

10 cm

15 cm   **8 cm**

Q5 Using the point O as centre of enlargement draw accurately and label:

a) the image $A_1B_1C_1$ of the triangle ABC after an enlargement scale factor 2

b) the image $A_2B_2C_2$ of the triangle ABC after an enlargement scale factor -1.

c) Which image is congruent to triangle ABC?

O•

A   B

C

For a length to area question, first find the scale factor between your two lengths and square it to find the scale factor between the two areas. Then multiply/divide your area by this new scale factor as necessary. It's the same method for everything, except you might need to cube, square root or cube root instead to find your new scale factor.

3D Pythagoras and Trigonometry

I bet when Pythagoras came up with his theorem he thought he was rather clever and everyone would like him for it. If only we could invent a time machine and go and tell him how he would be hated by school-goers the world round, maybe he would have thought better of it and gone for a cuppa instead.

Q1

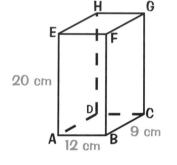

20 cm

12 cm   9 cm

This rectangular box is 20 cm by 12 cm by 9 cm. Calculate:
a) angle ABE
b) length AF
c) length DF
d) angle EBH.

Q2 This pyramid is on a square base of side 56 cm. Its vertical height is 32 cm. Calculate the length of:
a) the line from E to the mid-point of BC
b) the sloping edge BE.
c) Find the angle between BE and the base of the pyramid.

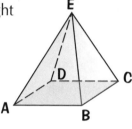

Q3 A rectangular box measures 20 cm by 30 cm by 8 cm. Calculate the lengths of:
a) the diagonal of each rectangular face
b) the diagonal through the centre of the box.

Q4 This cone has a perpendicular height of 9 cm. The centre of the base is O. The slant line from X makes an angle of 23° with the central axis. Calculate:
a) the radius of the base
b) the area of the base
c) the volume of the cone.

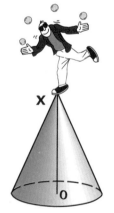

Q5 Cecil the shark has a wonky fin. When he swims it sticks out of the water at an angle. The plane BOC represents the water, and ABC represents Cecil's fin.
AOM = AMC = OMC = 90°, angle ABC = 55°.
BC = 60 cm, AB = 80 cm, CO = 22 cm.

What angle (AMO) does Cecil's fin make with the water?

Probability

There are two important rules you need to learn to answer these questions...

1) The OR rule: $P(A \text{ or } B) = P(A) + P(B)$ 2) The AND rule: $P(A \text{ and } B) = P(A) \times P(B)$

If you get stuck, try drawing a tree diagram. See pages 76-77 for some practice at using tree diagrams to calculate probabilities

Q1 **a)** What is the probability of randomly selecting either a black Ace or black King from an ordinary pack of playing cards?

You need the OR rule for this one.

b) If the entire suit of clubs is removed from a pack of cards, what is the probability of randomly selecting a red 7 from the remaining cards?

c) If all the 7s are also removed from the pack of cards, what is the probability of randomly selecting the 4 of diamonds?

Q2 Fabrizio is practising taking penalties. The probability that he misses the goal completely is $\frac{1}{8}$. The probability that the goalkeeper saves the penalty is $\frac{3}{8}$. The probability that he scores is $\frac{1}{2}$. Fabrizio takes two penalties.

a) Calculate the probability that Fabrizio fails to score with his two penalties.
b) Calculate the probability that he scores only one goal.
c) Calculate the probability that Fabrizio scores on neither or both of his 2 attempts.

Q3 Two different letters are written down at random. Each of the letters is one of the first nine letters of the alphabet. What is the probability that:

a) both letters are different vowels?
b) both letters are different consonants?
c) one of the letters is a vowel, but not both?

Notice that the question says "two different letters..." It's important.

Q4 Trevor and his 2 brothers and 5 friends are seated at random in a row of 8 seats at the cinema. What is the probability that Trevor has one brother on his immediate left and one on his immediate right?

Careful here — you have to include the probability that Trevor sits in one of the six middle seats.

Histograms

It's the <u>size that counts</u>... You've got to look at the <u>area</u> of the bars to find the frequency. That means looking at the <u>width</u> as well as the height.

Q1 The histogram below represents the age distribution of people who watch outdoor bog snorkelling. Given that there are 24 people in the 40 – 55 age range, find the number of people in all the other age ranges.

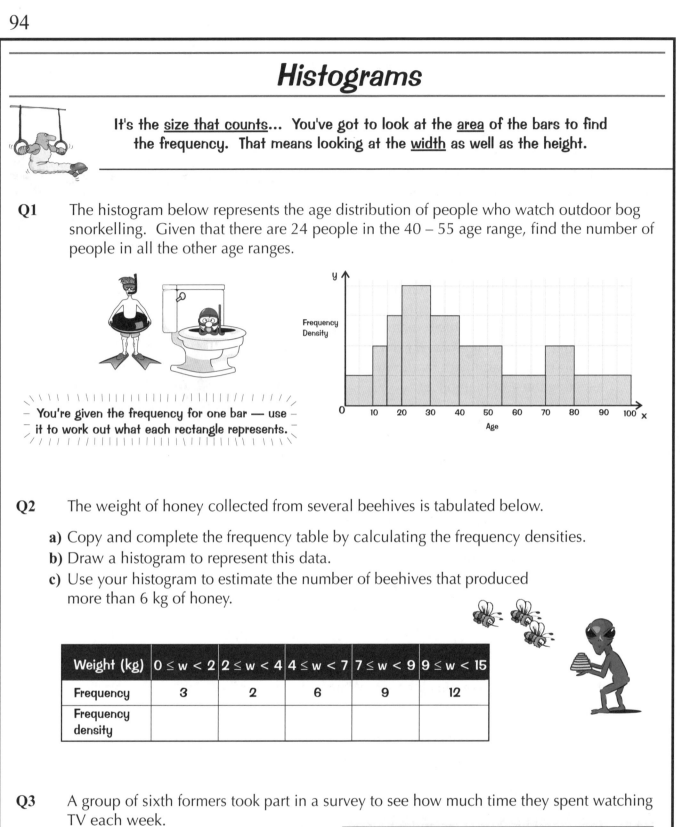

You're given the frequency for one bar — use it to work out what each rectangle represents.

Q2 The weight of honey collected from several beehives is tabulated below.

a) Copy and complete the frequency table by calculating the frequency densities.

b) Draw a histogram to represent this data.

c) Use your histogram to estimate the number of beehives that produced more than 6 kg of honey.

Weight (kg)	$0 \leq w < 2$	$2 \leq w < 4$	$4 \leq w < 7$	$7 \leq w < 9$	$9 \leq w < 15$
Frequency	3	2	6	9	12
Frequency density					

Q3 A group of sixth formers took part in a survey to see how much time they spent watching TV each week.

a) Copy and complete the table by filling in the frequency density column.

b) How many students took part in the survey?

c) Represent the data as a histogram.

d) Estimate the number of students that watch more than 7, but less than 13 hours each week.

No. of hours	Frequency	Frequency density
$0 \leq h < 1$	6	
$1 \leq h < 3$	13	
$3 \leq h < 5$	15	
$5 \leq h < 8$	9	
$8 \leq h < 10$	23	
$10 \leq h < 15$	25	
$15 \leq h < 20$	12	

Sampling Methods

Q1 Define:
a) random sampling
b) stratified sampling

You've also got to be able to spot problems and criticise sampling techniques —
basically, if you think it's a load of rubbish, you get the chance to say why.

Q2 Give a reason why the following methods of sampling are poor:
a) a survey carried out inside a newsagents concluded that 80% of the population buy a daily newspaper
b) a phone poll conducted at 11 am on a Sunday morning revealed that less than 2% of the population regularly go to church
c) 60% of the population were estimated to watch the 9 o'clock news each evening after a survey was carried out at a bridge club

Q3 Decide which of the following questions (if any) are suitable for a survey to find which of five desserts (cheesecake, fruit salad, sherry trifle, knickerbocker glory and chocolate cake) people like the most. Give a reason for each of your answers.
a) Do you like cheesecake, fruit salad, sherry trifle, knickerbocker glory or chocolate cake?
b) How often do you eat dessert?
c) Which is your favourite out of: cheesecake; fruit salad; sherry trifle; knickerbocker glory; chocolate cake?
d) What is your favourite dessert?
e) Is your favourite dessert: cheesecake; fruit salad; sherry trifle; knickerbocker glory; chocolate cake; none of these?

Q4 A newspaper contained the following article regarding the amount of exercise teenagers take outside school.

a) Suggest 3 questions that you could use in a survey to find out whether this is true at your school.
b) At a particular school there are 300 pupils in each of years 7 to 11. There are approximately equal numbers of girls and boys.
Describe how you would select 10% of the pupils for a stratified sample which is representative of all the pupils at the school.

Over half of all teenagers
do no exercise at all.
Only one in ten play
team sports or take part
in individual sports.

Compound Growth and Decay

Hey look — it's another of those "there is only one formula to learn and you use it for every question" topics. So I reckon you'd better learn The Formula then...

Q1 Calculate the amount in each account if:

$N = N_0 (1 + {}^r/_{100})^n$

a) £200 is invested for 10 years at 9% compound interest per annum
b) £500 is invested for 3 years at 7% compound interest per annum
c) £750 is invested for 30 months at 8% compound interest per annum
d) £1000 is invested for 15 months at 6.5% compound interest per annum.

Q2 A colony of bacteria grows at the compound rate of 12% per hour. Initially there are 200 bacteria.

a) How many will there be after 3 hours?
b) How many will there be after 1 day?
c) After how many whole hours will there be at least 4000 bacteria? (Solve this by trial and error.)

Q3 A radioactive element was observed every day and the mass remaining was measured. Initially there was 9 kg, but this decreased at the compound rate of 3% per day. How much radioactive element will be left after:

a) 3 days   b) 6 days   c) 1 week   d) 4 weeks?

Q4 Money is invested on the stock market. During a recession the value of the shares fall by 2% per week. Find the value of the stock if:

a) £2000 was invested for a fortnight
b) £30,000 was invested for four weeks
c) £500 was invested for 7 weeks
d) £100,000 was invested for a year.

Q5 Mrs Smith decides to invest £7000 in a savings account. She has the choice of putting all her money into an account paying 5% compound interest per annum or she can put half of her investment into an account paying 6% compound interest per annum and the remaining half into an account paying 4% per annum.

If she left the investment alone for 3 years, which is her best option and by how much?

Q6 The population of a country is 16 million, and the annual compound growth rate is estimated to be 1.3%. Predict the country's population in:

a) 4 years' time   b) 20 years' time.

Q7 Property prices in an area have depreciated by 5% per year. Calculate the expected value the following:

a) a house bought for £45,000, 3 years ago
b) a bungalow bought for £58,000, 4 years ago
c) a flat bought for £52,000, six months ago
d) a factory bought for £350,000, 7 years ago.

Recurring Decimals

For this page you'll need to know...

> 1) what <u>recurring decimals</u> are and the <u>dot notation</u> for them,
> 2) how to <u>convert</u> terminating and recurring decimals into fractions
> 3) how to <u>tell</u> if a fraction will be recurring or terminating decimal.

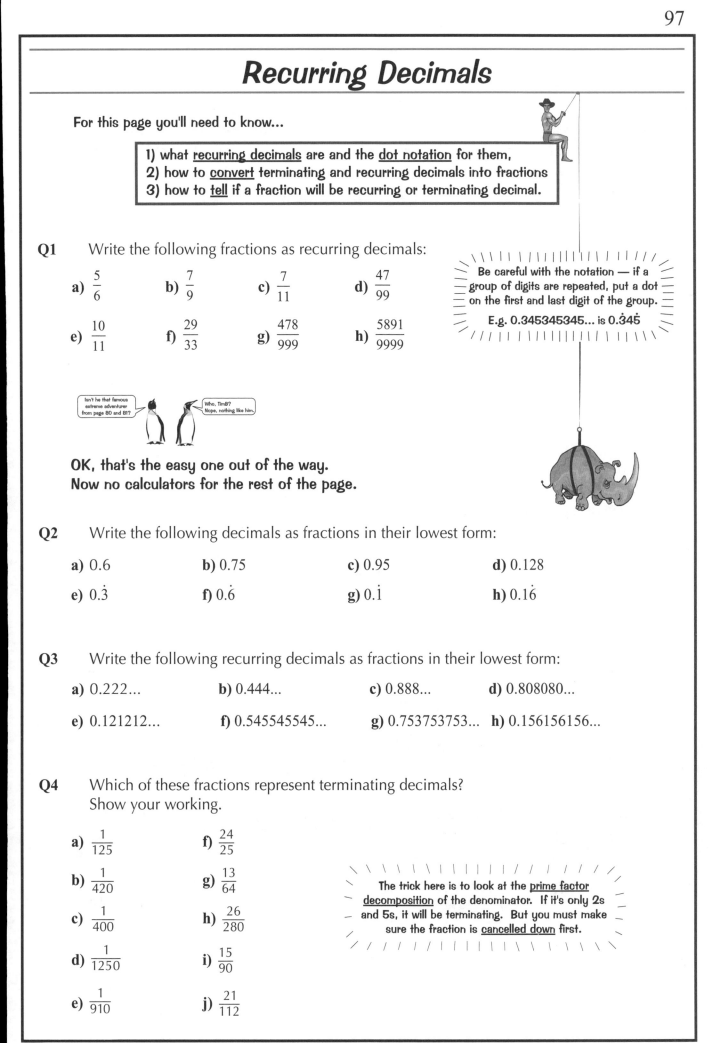

Q1 Write the following fractions as recurring decimals:

a) $\dfrac{5}{6}$ b) $\dfrac{7}{9}$ c) $\dfrac{7}{11}$ d) $\dfrac{47}{99}$

e) $\dfrac{10}{11}$ f) $\dfrac{29}{33}$ g) $\dfrac{478}{999}$ h) $\dfrac{5891}{9999}$

Be careful with the notation — if a group of digits are repeated, put a dot on the first and last digit of the group. E.g. 0.345345345... is $0.\dot{3}4\dot{5}$

Isn't he that famous extreme adventurer from page 80 and 81?

Who, TimB? Nope, nothing like him.

OK, that's the easy one out of the way.
Now no calculators for the rest of the page.

Q2 Write the following decimals as fractions in their lowest form:

a) 0.6   b) 0.75   c) 0.95   d) 0.128

e) $0.\dot{3}$ f) $0.\dot{6}$ g) $0.\dot{1}$ h) $0.1\dot{6}$

Q3 Write the following recurring decimals as fractions in their lowest form:

a) 0.222...   b) 0.444...   c) 0.888...   d) 0.808080...

e) 0.121212...   f) 0.545545545...   g) 0.753753753...   h) 0.156156156...

Q4 Which of these fractions represent terminating decimals?
Show your working.

a) $\dfrac{1}{125}$ f) $\dfrac{24}{25}$

b) $\dfrac{1}{420}$ g) $\dfrac{13}{64}$

c) $\dfrac{1}{400}$ h) $\dfrac{26}{280}$

d) $\dfrac{1}{1250}$ i) $\dfrac{15}{90}$

e) $\dfrac{1}{910}$ j) $\dfrac{21}{112}$

The trick here is to look at the <u>prime factor decomposition</u> of the denominator. If it's only 2s and 5s, it will be terminating. But you must make sure the fraction is <u>cancelled down</u> first.

Surds

I think the idea of rational and irrational numbers is a bit odd.
Basically, a <u>rational</u> number is either a <u>whole</u> number or one you can write as a <u>fraction</u>.
An <u>irrational</u> number... you guessed it... is <u>not</u> whole and <u>can't</u> be written as a fraction.

Q1   Write down a rational and an irrational number both greater than $\sqrt{5}$ and less than 5.

Q2   Write down a value of x for which $x^{1/2}$ is:
a) irrational
b) rational

> Watch out for those roots — they're not always irrational. For example, the square root of a square number will be rational.

Q3   Which of the following are rational and which are irrational?

a) $(\sqrt{3})^1$ **b)** $(\sqrt{3})^2$ **c)** $(\sqrt{3})^3$ **d)** $(\sqrt{3})^4$

e) $16^{1/2}$ **f)** $16^{1/3}$ **g)** $16^{1/4}$

Q4   **a)** Write down a rational number which is greater than 1 but less than 2.
b) Write down an irrational number which lies between 1 and 2.
c) If P is a non-zero rational number, is 1/P also a rational number?
Clearly show your reasoning.

Q5   If $x = 2$, $y = \sqrt{3}$ and $z = 2\sqrt{2}$, which of the following expressions
are rational and which are irrational? Show your working.

a) xyz **b)** $(xyz)^2$ **c)** $x + yz$ **d)** $\dfrac{yz}{2\sqrt{3x}}$

Q6   Simplify:

> Remember — $\sqrt{a} \times \sqrt{b} = \sqrt{(ab)}$.

a) $\sqrt{5} \times \sqrt{3}$ **b)** $\dfrac{\sqrt{20}}{\sqrt{5}}$ **c)** $\sqrt{4} - \sqrt{1}$ **d)** $\left(\dfrac{\sqrt{5}}{\sqrt{2}}\right)^2$

e) $\left(\sqrt{x}\right)^2$ **f)** $\sqrt{x^2}$ **g)** $\sqrt{8} \times \sqrt{8}$ **h)** $\sqrt{18} - \sqrt{9}$

Q7   Rationalise the denominators
and then simplify if necessary:

> Rationalising the denominator means getting rid of the square root signs on the bottom of fractions.

a) $\dfrac{1}{\sqrt{2}}$ **b)** $\dfrac{2}{\sqrt{8}}$ **c)** $\dfrac{a}{\frac{\sqrt{40}}{2}}$ **d)** $\dfrac{x}{\sqrt{xy}}$

e) $\dfrac{1}{1+\sqrt{2}}$ **f)** $\dfrac{6}{3+\sqrt{3}}$ **g)** $\dfrac{2}{1+\sqrt{6}}$ **h)** $\dfrac{5+\sqrt{5}}{5-\sqrt{5}}$

Algebraic Fractions

Before you start, if you think you could do with some general algebra practice, look back at p83. Now, this page is all about fractions of the algebra variety... or algebra of the fraction variety, if you like. Remember — the rules are just the same as for normal fractions.

Q1 Multiply out the following, simplifying your answers:

a) $\dfrac{x^2}{y} \times \dfrac{2}{x^3}$

b) $\dfrac{2x}{y^2} \times \dfrac{y^3}{4x^3}$

c) $\dfrac{10z^3}{xy} \times \dfrac{4x^3}{5z}$

It helps if you can cancel some factors before multiplying.

d) $\dfrac{4}{x} \times \dfrac{x^3}{2} \times \dfrac{x}{10}$

e) $\dfrac{400d^4}{51e^5} \times \dfrac{102d^2e^4}{800e^2f}$

f) $\dfrac{x^{\frac{2}{3}}}{y^{\frac{1}{3}}} \times \dfrac{x^{\frac{1}{3}}}{y^{-\frac{4}{3}}}$

Q2 Divide the following, leaving your answer as simplified as possible:

a) $\dfrac{4x^3}{y} \div \dfrac{2x}{y^2}$

b) $\dfrac{e^2f^2}{5} \div \dfrac{ef}{10}$

c) $\dfrac{25a^3}{b^3} \div \dfrac{5}{b^2}$

d) $\dfrac{ab}{c} \div \dfrac{b}{c}$

e) $\dfrac{5x^3}{y} \div \dfrac{1}{y}$

f) $\dfrac{x^{\frac{2}{3}}}{y^{\frac{1}{3}}} \div xy^{-\frac{2}{3}}$

Q3 Do these additions and subtractions, simplifying your answers:

a) $\dfrac{3}{2x} + \dfrac{y}{2x}$

b) $\dfrac{1}{x} + \dfrac{y}{x}$

c) $\dfrac{5x+2}{x} + \dfrac{2x+4}{x}$

d) $\dfrac{2x}{3} + \dfrac{2x}{4}$

e) $\dfrac{4x}{3} - \dfrac{5y}{3}$

f) $\dfrac{10+x^2}{4x} - \dfrac{x^2+11}{4x}$

g) $\dfrac{4x+3}{y} - \dfrac{4}{y}$

h) $\dfrac{2x}{3} - \dfrac{y}{6}$

i) $\dfrac{2b}{a} - \dfrac{b}{7}$

Q4 Solve the following equations for x:

a) $\dfrac{20x^4y^2z^3}{7xy^5} \times \dfrac{14y^3}{40x^2z^3} = 5$

b) $\dfrac{48x^5y^2}{12z^3} \div \dfrac{16x^2y^2}{z^3} = 2$

c) $\dfrac{1}{x-3} + \dfrac{x}{x-4} = 1$

d) $\dfrac{1}{x} + \dfrac{3x}{x+2} = 3$

e) $\dfrac{1}{x+2} + \dfrac{1}{x-1} = 1$

f) $\dfrac{3}{x+5} + \dfrac{2}{x-5} = 1$

The last two parts are tricky. You'll need to solve a quadratic equation — see p101.

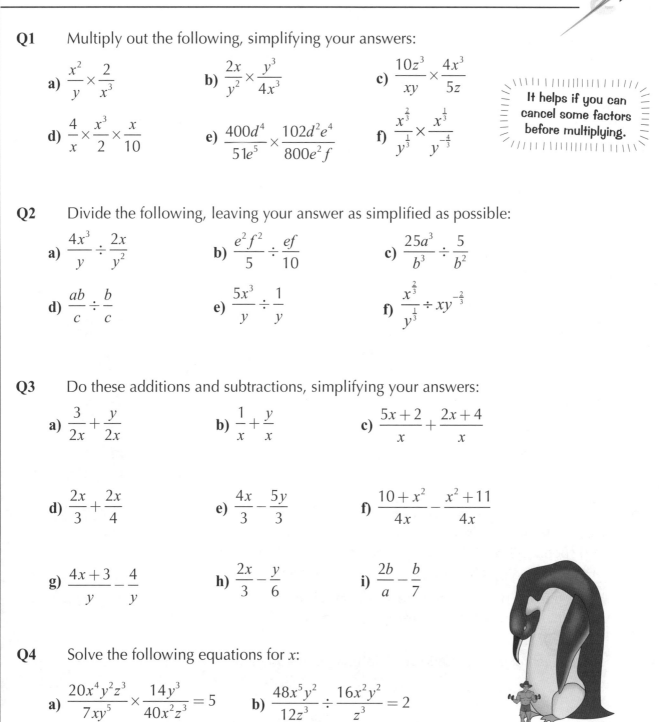

Simultaneous Equations

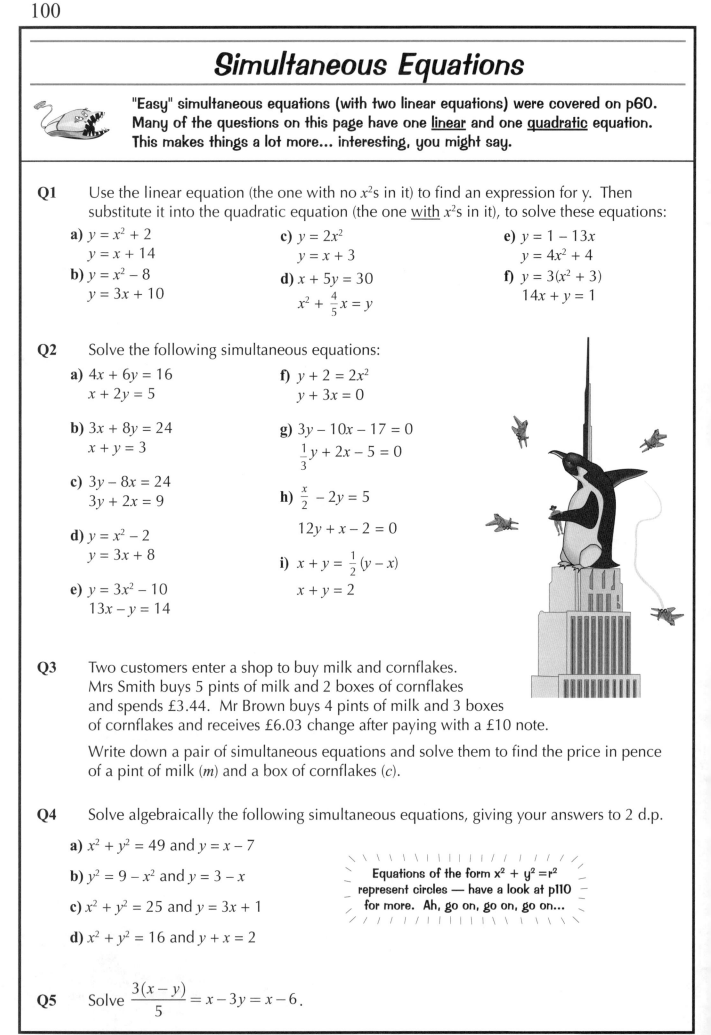

"Easy" simultaneous equations (with two linear equations) were covered on p60. Many of the questions on this page have one <u>linear</u> and one <u>quadratic</u> equation. This makes things a lot more... interesting, you might say.

Q1 Use the linear equation (the one with no x^2s in it) to find an expression for y. Then substitute it into the quadratic equation (the one <u>with</u> x^2s in it), to solve these equations:

a) $y = x^2 + 2$
$y = x + 14$

b) $y = x^2 - 8$
$y = 3x + 10$

c) $y = 2x^2$
$y = x + 3$

d) $x + 5y = 30$
$x^2 + \frac{4}{5}x = y$

e) $y = 1 - 13x$
$y = 4x^2 + 4$

f) $y = 3(x^2 + 3)$
$14x + y = 1$

Q2 Solve the following simultaneous equations:

a) $4x + 6y = 16$
$x + 2y = 5$

b) $3x + 8y = 24$
$x + y = 3$

c) $3y - 8x = 24$
$3y + 2x = 9$

d) $y = x^2 - 2$
$y = 3x + 8$

e) $y = 3x^2 - 10$
$13x - y = 14$

f) $y + 2 = 2x^2$
$y + 3x = 0$

g) $3y - 10x - 17 = 0$
$\frac{1}{3}y + 2x - 5 = 0$

h) $\frac{x}{2} - 2y = 5$
$12y + x - 2 = 0$

i) $x + y = \frac{1}{2}(y - x)$
$x + y = 2$

Q3 Two customers enter a shop to buy milk and cornflakes. Mrs Smith buys 5 pints of milk and 2 boxes of cornflakes and spends £3.44. Mr Brown buys 4 pints of milk and 3 boxes of cornflakes and receives £6.03 change after paying with a £10 note.

Write down a pair of simultaneous equations and solve them to find the price in pence of a pint of milk (*m*) and a box of cornflakes (*c*).

Q4 Solve algebraically the following simultaneous equations, giving your answers to 2 d.p.

a) $x^2 + y^2 = 49$ and $y = x - 7$

b) $y^2 = 9 - x^2$ and $y = 3 - x$

c) $x^2 + y^2 = 25$ and $y = 3x + 1$

d) $x^2 + y^2 = 16$ and $y + x = 2$

Equations of the form $x^2 + y^2 = r^2$ represent circles — have a look at p110 for more. Ah, go on, go on, go on...

Q5 Solve $\frac{3(x - y)}{5} = x - 3y = x - 6$.

The Quadratic Formula

Q1 Find the two values, to 2 d.p, given by each of the following expressions:

a) $\dfrac{2 \pm \sqrt{3}}{2}$

b) $\dfrac{4 \pm \sqrt{10}}{3}$

c) $\dfrac{-2 \pm \sqrt{27}}{2}$

d) $\dfrac{-3 \pm \sqrt{42}}{3}$

e) $\dfrac{-10 \pm \sqrt{160}}{5}$

f) $\dfrac{-27 \pm \sqrt{10}}{2}$

g) $\dfrac{-8 \pm \sqrt{9.5}}{2.4}$

h) $\dfrac{10 \pm \sqrt{88.4}}{23.2}$

Q2 The following quadratics can be solved by factorisation, but practise using the formula to solve them. Give your answers to 2 d.p. where appropriate.

a) $x^2 + 8x + 12 = 0$

b) $6x^2 - x - 2 = 0$

c) $4x^2 - 15x + 9 = 0$

d) $x^2 - 3x = 0$

e) $4x^2 + 8x - 12 = 0$

f) $3x^2 - 11x - 20 = 0$

g) $1 - 5x + 6x^2 = 0$

h) $3(x^2 + 2x) = 9$

i) $x^2 + 4(x - 3) = 0$

j) $x^2 = 2(4 - x)$

> **Step number 1...**
> Write out the formula.

> **Step number 2...**
> Write down values for a, b and c.

> **Step number 3...** sub a, b and c into the formula. Make sure you divide the <u>whole</u> of the top line by <u>2a</u> — not just ½ of it.

Q3 Solve the following quadratics using the formula.
Give your answers to no more than two decimal places.

a) $x^2 + 3x - 1 = 0$

b) $x^2 - 2x - 6 = 0$

c) $x^2 + x - 1 = 0$

d) $x^2 + 6x + 3 = 0$

e) $x^2 - x - 1 = 0$

f) $3x^2 + 10x - 8 = 0$

g) $x^2 + 4x + 2 = 0$

h) $x^2 - 6x - 8 = 0$

i) $x^2 + 3x - 5 = 0$

j) $7x^2 - 15x + 6 = 0$

k) $2x^2 + 6x - 3 = 0$

l) $2x^2 - 7x + 4 = 0$

Q4 Rearrange the following in the form "$ax^2 + bx + c = 0$" and then solve by the quadratic formula. Give your answers to two decimal places.

a) $x^2 = 8 - 3x$

b) $(x + 2)^2 - 3 = 0$

c) $3x(x - 1) = 5$

d) $2x(x + 4) = 1$

e) $x^2 = 4(x + 1)$

f) $(2x - 1)^2 = 5$

g) $3x^2 + 2x = 6$

h) $(x + 2)(x + 3) = 5$

i) $(x - 2)(2x - 1) = 3$

j) $2x + \frac{4}{x} = 7$

k) $(x - \frac{1}{2})^2 = \frac{1}{4}$

l) $4x(x - 2) = -3$

Q5 The sides of a right angled triangle are as shown.
Use Pythagoras' theorem to form a quadratic
equation in x and then solve it to find x.

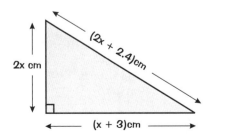

Completing the Square

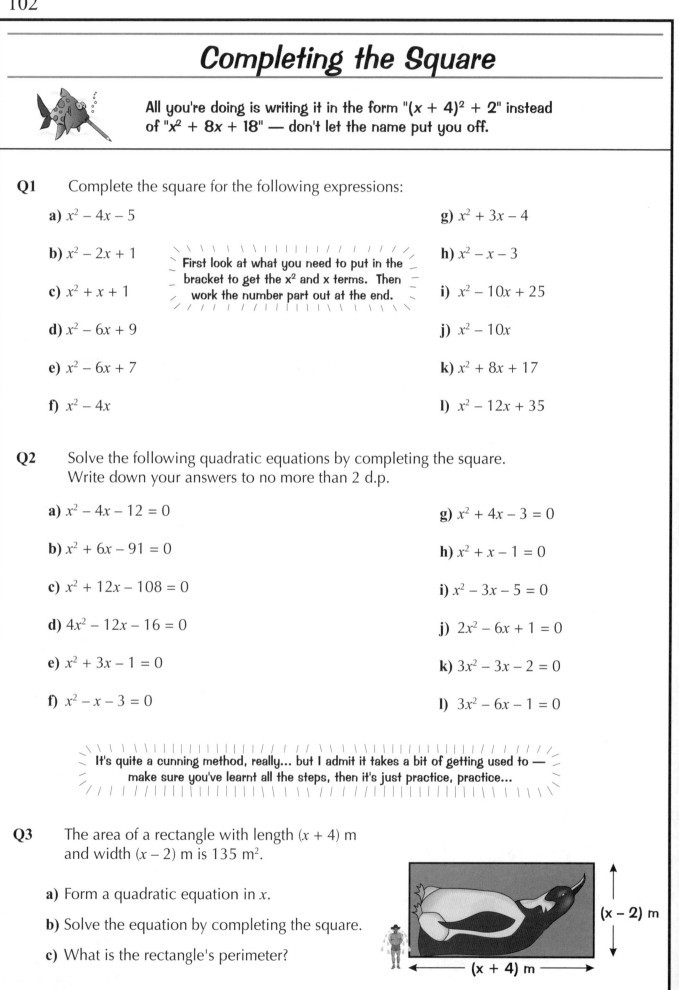

All you're doing is writing it in the form "$(x + 4)^2 + 2$" instead of "$x^2 + 8x + 18$" — don't let the name put you off.

Q1 Complete the square for the following expressions:

a) $x^2 - 4x - 5$

b) $x^2 - 2x + 1$

c) $x^2 + x + 1$

d) $x^2 - 6x + 9$

e) $x^2 - 6x + 7$

f) $x^2 - 4x$

First look at what you need to put in the bracket to get the x^2 and x terms. Then work the number part out at the end.

g) $x^2 + 3x - 4$

h) $x^2 - x - 3$

i) $x^2 - 10x + 25$

j) $x^2 - 10x$

k) $x^2 + 8x + 17$

l) $x^2 - 12x + 35$

Q2 Solve the following quadratic equations by completing the square. Write down your answers to no more than 2 d.p.

a) $x^2 - 4x - 12 = 0$

b) $x^2 + 6x - 91 = 0$

c) $x^2 + 12x - 108 = 0$

d) $4x^2 - 12x - 16 = 0$

e) $x^2 + 3x - 1 = 0$

f) $x^2 - x - 3 = 0$

g) $x^2 + 4x - 3 = 0$

h) $x^2 + x - 1 = 0$

i) $x^2 - 3x - 5 = 0$

j) $2x^2 - 6x + 1 = 0$

k) $3x^2 - 3x - 2 = 0$

l) $3x^2 - 6x - 1 = 0$

It's quite a cunning method, really... but I admit it takes a bit of getting used to — make sure you've learnt all the steps, then it's just practice, practice...

Q3 The area of a rectangle with length $(x + 4)$ m and width $(x - 2)$ m is 135 m².

a) Form a quadratic equation in x.

b) Solve the equation by completing the square.

c) What is the rectangle's perimeter?

$(x - 2)$ m

$(x + 4)$ m

The Sine and Cosine Rules

Make sure you know the Sine Rule and <u>both forms</u> of the Cosine Rule.
The one to use depends on which angles and sides you're given.

Q1 Calculate the lengths required to 3 s.f.

Q2 Calculate the angles required, to the nearest degree.

Q3 Calculate the lettered sides and angles.

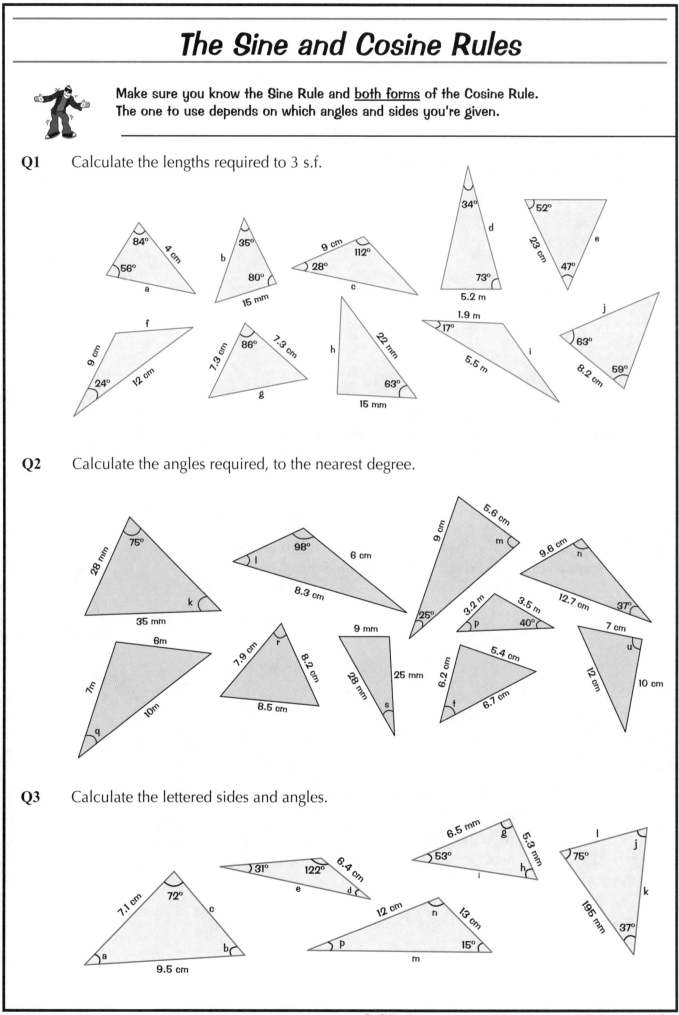

The Sine and Cosine Rules

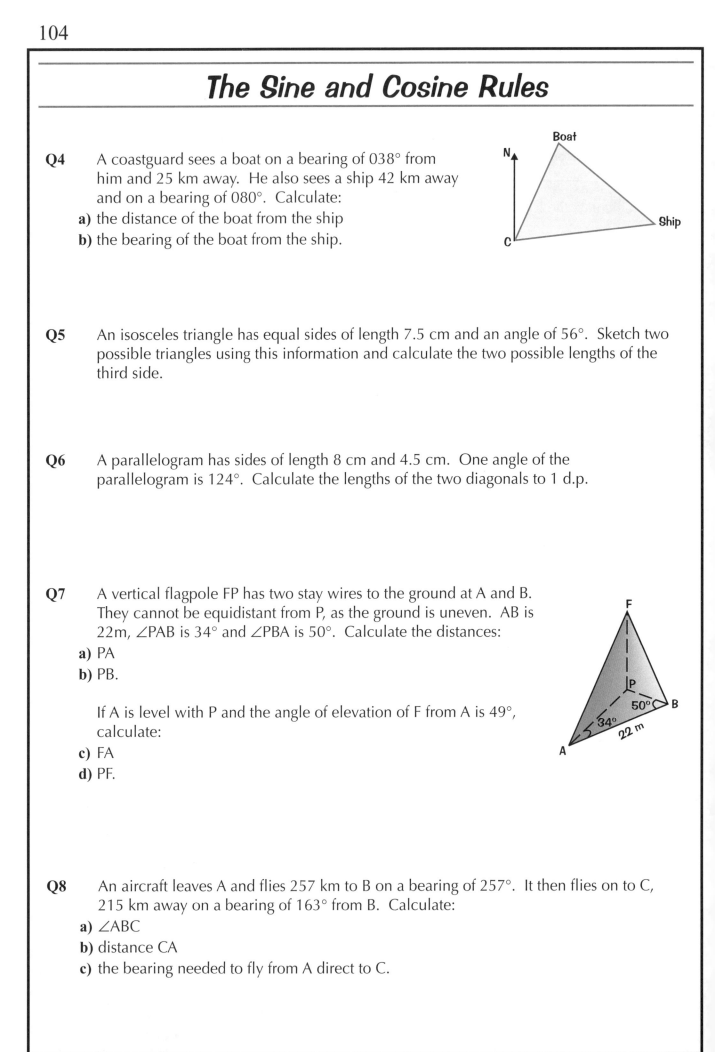

Q4 A coastguard sees a boat on a bearing of 038° from him and 25 km away. He also sees a ship 42 km away and on a bearing of 080°. Calculate:

a) the distance of the boat from the ship

b) the bearing of the boat from the ship.

Q5 An isosceles triangle has equal sides of length 7.5 cm and an angle of 56°. Sketch two possible triangles using this information and calculate the two possible lengths of the third side.

Q6 A parallelogram has sides of length 8 cm and 4.5 cm. One angle of the parallelogram is 124°. Calculate the lengths of the two diagonals to 1 d.p.

Q7 A vertical flagpole FP has two stay wires to the ground at A and B. They cannot be equidistant from P, as the ground is uneven. AB is 22m, ∠PAB is 34° and ∠PBA is 50°. Calculate the distances:

a) PA

b) PB.

If A is level with P and the angle of elevation of F from A is 49°, calculate:

c) FA

d) PF.

Q8 An aircraft leaves A and flies 257 km to B on a bearing of 257°. It then flies on to C, 215 km away on a bearing of 163° from B. Calculate:

a) ∠ABC

b) distance CA

c) the bearing needed to fly from A direct to C.

The Graphs of Sin, Cos and Tan

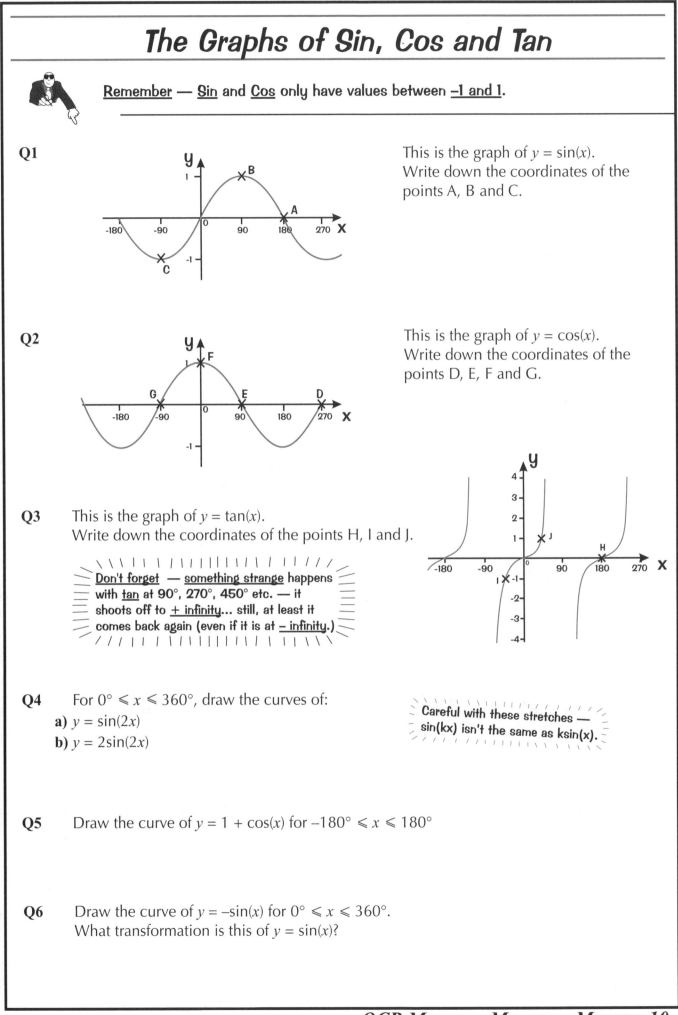

Remember — <u>Sin</u> and <u>Cos</u> only have values between <u>–1 and 1</u>.

Q1

This is the graph of $y = \sin(x)$.
Write down the coordinates of the points A, B and C.

Q2

This is the graph of $y = \cos(x)$.
Write down the coordinates of the points D, E, F and G.

Q3 This is the graph of $y = \tan(x)$.
Write down the coordinates of the points H, I and J.

<u>Don't forget</u> — <u>something strange</u> happens with <u>tan</u> at 90°, 270°, 450° etc. — it shoots off to ± infinity... still, at least it comes back again (even if it is at <u>– infinity.</u>)

Q4 For $0° \leqslant x \leqslant 360°$, draw the curves of:
a) $y = \sin(2x)$
b) $y = 2\sin(2x)$

Careful with these stretches — sin(kx) isn't the same as ksin(x).

Q5 Draw the curve of $y = 1 + \cos(x)$ for $-180° \leqslant x \leqslant 180°$

Q6 Draw the curve of $y = -\sin(x)$ for $0° \leqslant x \leqslant 360°$.
What transformation is this of $y = \sin(x)$?

The Graphs of Sin, Cos and Tan

Q7 The graph of $y = \sin(x)$ is shown below for $-720° \leq x \leq 720°$.

Graph of y = sin x   **-720° ⩽ x ⩽ 720°**

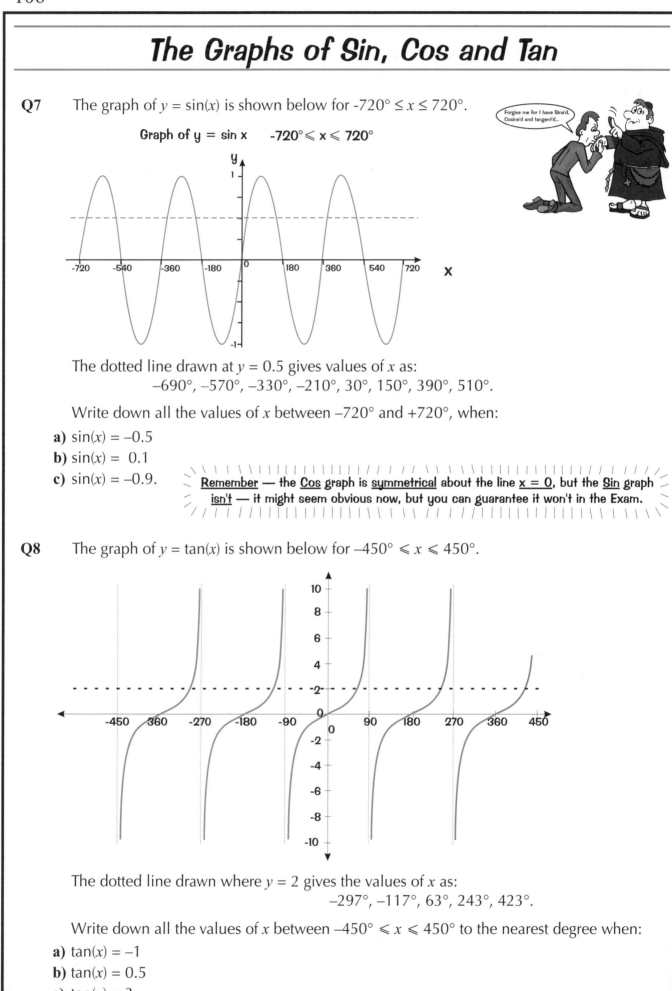

The dotted line drawn at $y = 0.5$ gives values of x as:
$-690°, -570°, -330°, -210°, 30°, 150°, 390°, 510°$.

Write down all the values of x between $-720°$ and $+720°$, when:

a) $\sin(x) = -0.5$

b) $\sin(x) = 0.1$

c) $\sin(x) = -0.9$.
Remember — the Cos graph is symmetrical about the line x = 0, but the Sin graph isn't — it might seem obvious now, but you can guarantee it won't in the Exam.

Q8 The graph of $y = \tan(x)$ is shown below for $-450° \leq x \leq 450°$.

The dotted line drawn where $y = 2$ gives the values of x as:
$-297°, -117°, 63°, 243°, 423°$.

Write down all the values of x between $-450° \leq x \leq 450°$ to the nearest degree when:

a) $\tan(x) = -1$

b) $\tan(x) = 0.5$

c) $\tan(x) = 3$.

The Graphs of Sin, Cos and Tan

Q9 Write down 4 possible values of x, to the nearest degree, if:

a) $\sin(x) = 0.39$

b) $\cos(x) = 0.39$

c) $\tan(x) = -39$.

You've got to know how often these graphs repeat themselves.

Q10 Which of the graphs $y = \sin(x)$, $y = \cos(x)$, $y = \tan(x)$ go through the points labelled A, B, C, ...J? (Sometimes it is more than one.)

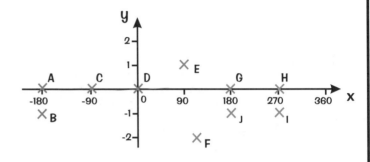

Q11 Plot the points given in this table.

X	0	90	180	270	360
y	2	1	0	1	2

Write down an equation for the curve you have plotted.

Q12 Draw accurately the graph of $y = 10\cos(x)$ for $-180° \leqslant x \leqslant 180°$.

On the same axes draw the graph of $10y = x + 20$.

Write down the coordinates of where the graphs cross. Show that this can be used to find a solution to the equation:

$$20 = 100\cos(x) - x.$$

Q13 Complete this table of values for $\sin(x)$ and $(\sin(x))^2$.

X	0	10	20	30	40	50	60	70	80	90
sin x		0.17		0.5						1
$(\sin x)^2$		0.03		0.25						1

Draw axes for the graph from $-180° \leqslant x \leqslant 180°$.

Plot the points for $(\sin(x))^2$.

From your knowledge of sin graphs, draw the rest of the graph for the limits given.

Q14 Draw accurately the graph of $y = \tan(x)$ for $0° \leqslant x \leqslant 360°$. Let the y-axis have values -12 to $+12$.

On the same axis, draw the graph of $10y - x = 25$.

Use your graphs to find an approximate solution to the equation $x = 10\tan(x) - 25$.

Graph Transformations

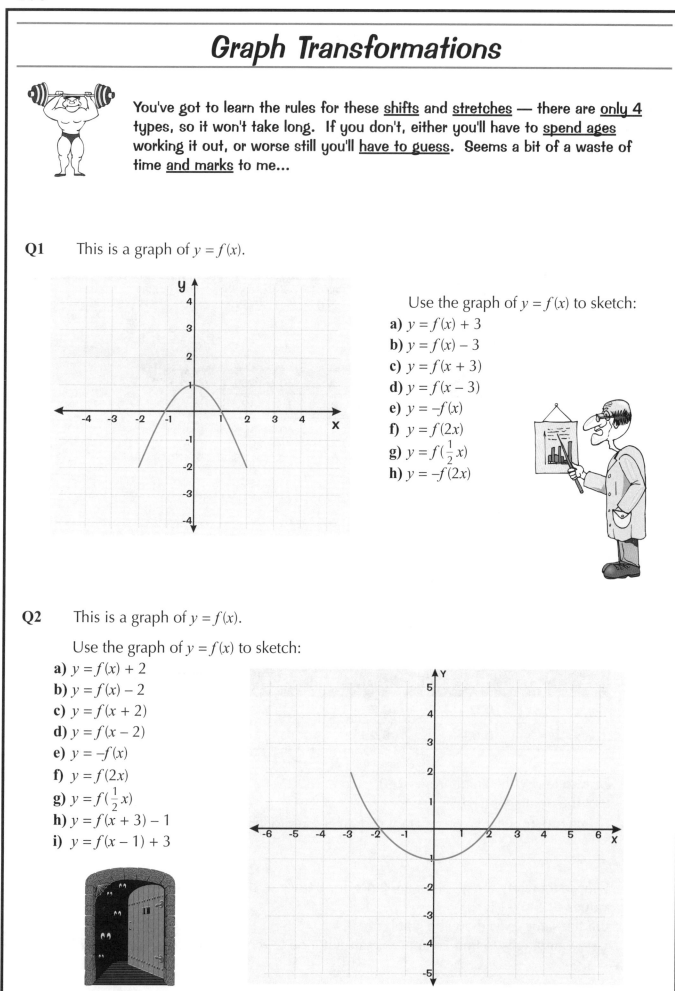

You've got to learn the rules for these <u>shifts</u> and <u>stretches</u> — there are <u>only 4</u> types, so it won't take long. If you don't, either you'll have to <u>spend ages</u> working it out, or worse still you'll <u>have to guess</u>. Seems a bit of a waste of time <u>and marks</u> to me...

Q1 This is a graph of $y = f(x)$.

Use the graph of $y = f(x)$ to sketch:
a) $y = f(x) + 3$
b) $y = f(x) - 3$
c) $y = f(x + 3)$
d) $y = f(x - 3)$
e) $y = -f(x)$
f) $y = f(2x)$
g) $y = f(\frac{1}{2}x)$
h) $y = -f(2x)$

Q2 This is a graph of $y = f(x)$.

Use the graph of $y = f(x)$ to sketch:
a) $y = f(x) + 2$
b) $y = f(x) - 2$
c) $y = f(x + 2)$
d) $y = f(x - 2)$
e) $y = -f(x)$
f) $y = f(2x)$
g) $y = f(\frac{1}{2}x)$
h) $y = f(x + 3) - 1$
i) $y = f(x - 1) + 3$

Graph Transformations

Q3 This is the graph of $y = \sin(x)$:

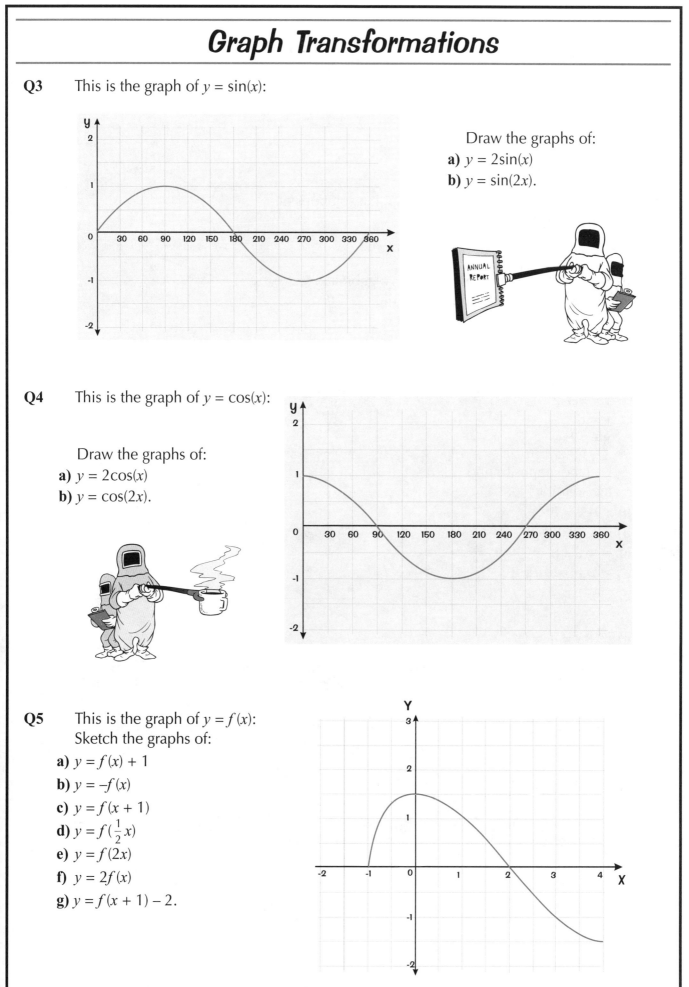

Draw the graphs of:
a) $y = 2\sin(x)$
b) $y = \sin(2x)$.

Q4 This is the graph of $y = \cos(x)$:

Draw the graphs of:
a) $y = 2\cos(x)$
b) $y = \cos(2x)$.

Q5 This is the graph of $y = f(x)$:
Sketch the graphs of:

a) $y = f(x) + 1$
b) $y = -f(x)$
c) $y = f(x + 1)$
d) $y = f(\frac{1}{2}x)$
e) $y = f(2x)$
f) $y = 2f(x)$
g) $y = f(x + 1) - 2$.

More Graphs

There's two special types of graph you need to know for module 10: 1) circles ($x^2 + y^2 = r^2$, where r is the radius) 2) exponential graphs (e.g. $y = k^x$, where k is a fixed number.)

Q1 The diagram shows the straight line $3y = x - 3$ and the circle $x^2 + y^2 = 25$.

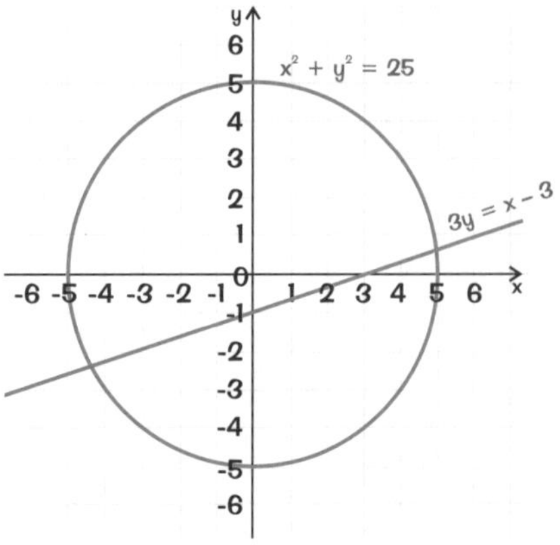

a) Use the graph to estimate to 1 d.p. the solutions of the simultaneous equations

$$3y = x - 3 \qquad x^2 + y^2 = 25$$

b) Solve the simultaneous equations algebraically, giving your answers correct to 2 d.p.

Q2 The diagram shows the graphs:
$y = x^2 - x$
$y = x + 2$
$y = 8$
$y = -2x + 4$

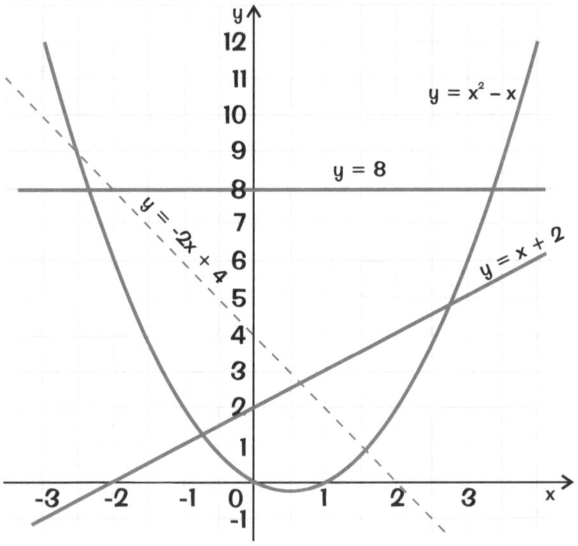

Use the graphs to find the solutions to:
a) $x^2 - x = 0$
b) $x^2 - x = x + 2$
c) $x^2 - x = 8$
d) $x^2 - x = -2x + 4$
e) $-2x + 4 = x + 2$
f) $x^2 - x - 8 = 0$
g) $x^2 + x = 4$

These equations look a bit nasty, but they're just made up of the equations you've got graphs for. And you know how to do the rest of it, don't you...

Q3 Using graph paper, accurately draw the graphs of the following pairs of equations. Use the graphs to estimate the solutions to each pair of equations to 1 d.p.

a) $x^2 + y^2 = 36$ and $y = x - 3$
b) $y^2 = 16 - x^2$ and $y = 2x + 2$

Q4 Using graph paper, draw axes for x-values from -5 to 5 and y-values from 0 to 100. On these axes, draw the graphs of these equations:

a) $y = 2^x$
b) $y = 3^x$
c) $y = 2^{-x}$

Q5 a) Using graph paper, draw x-axis from 0 to 6 and y-axis from 0 to 60.

b) Draw the graphs of the following equations:

$$y = 30 - 10x \qquad y = 2^x$$

b) Use your diagram to estimate the solution to the equation $30 - 10x = 2^x$.

Volume and Surface Area

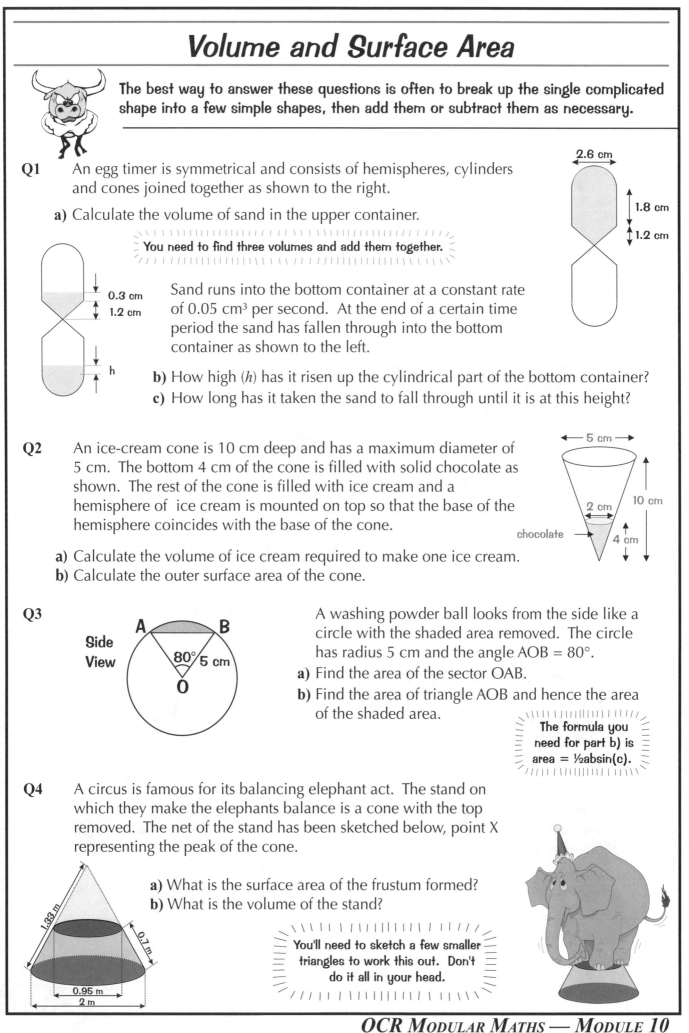

The best way to answer these questions is often to break up the single complicated shape into a few simple shapes, then add them or subtract them as necessary.

Q1 An egg timer is symmetrical and consists of hemispheres, cylinders and cones joined together as shown to the right.

2.6 cm
1.8 cm
1.2 cm

a) Calculate the volume of sand in the upper container.

You need to find three volumes and add them together.

0.3 cm
1.2 cm

Sand runs into the bottom container at a constant rate of 0.05 cm³ per second. At the end of a certain time period the sand has fallen through into the bottom container as shown to the left.

h

b) How high (*h*) has it risen up the cylindrical part of the bottom container?
c) How long has it taken the sand to fall through until it is at this height?

Q2 An ice-cream cone is 10 cm deep and has a maximum diameter of 5 cm. The bottom 4 cm of the cone is filled with solid chocolate as shown. The rest of the cone is filled with ice cream and a hemisphere of ice cream is mounted on top so that the base of the hemisphere coincides with the base of the cone.

5 cm
2 cm
10 cm
chocolate
4 cm

a) Calculate the volume of ice cream required to make one ice cream.
b) Calculate the outer surface area of the cone.

Q3

Side View

A   B
80° 5 cm
O

A washing powder ball looks from the side like a circle with the shaded area removed. The circle has radius 5 cm and the angle AOB = 80°.

a) Find the area of the sector OAB.
b) Find the area of triangle AOB and hence the area of the shaded area.

The formula you need for part b) is area = ½absin(c).

Q4 A circus is famous for its balancing elephant act. The stand on which they make the elephants balance is a cone with the top removed. The net of the stand has been sketched below, point X representing the peak of the cone.

a) What is the surface area of the frustum formed?
b) What is the volume of the stand?

1.33 m
0.7 m
0.95 m
2 m

You'll need to sketch a few smaller triangles to work this out. Don't do it all in your head.

Congruence

Q1 Which pair of triangles are congruent? Explain why.

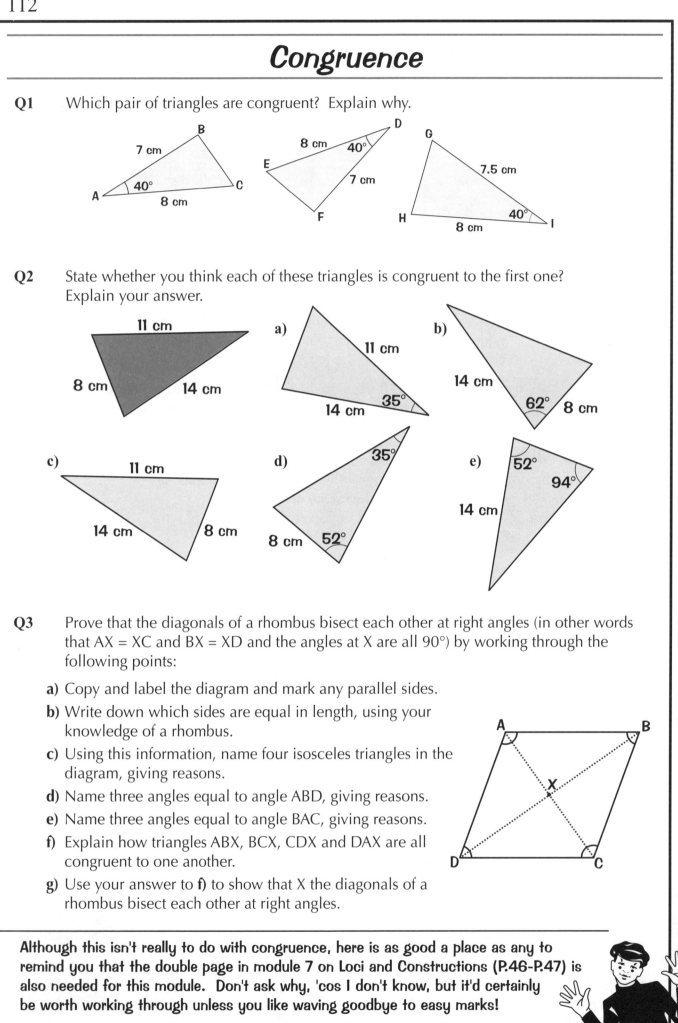

Q2 State whether you think each of these triangles is congruent to the first one? Explain your answer.

Q3 Prove that the diagonals of a rhombus bisect each other at right angles (in other words that AX = XC and BX = XD and the angles at X are all 90°) by working through the following points:

a) Copy and label the diagram and mark any parallel sides.

b) Write down which sides are equal in length, using your knowledge of a rhombus.

c) Using this information, name four isosceles triangles in the diagram, giving reasons.

d) Name three angles equal to angle ABD, giving reasons.

e) Name three angles equal to angle BAC, giving reasons.

f) Explain how triangles ABX, BCX, CDX and DAX are all congruent to one another.

g) Use your answer to **f)** to show that X the diagonals of a rhombus bisect each other at right angles.

Although this isn't really to do with congruence, here is as good a place as any to remind you that the double page in module 7 on Loci and Constructions (P.46-P.47) is also needed for this module. Don't ask why, 'cos I don't know, but it'd certainly be worth working through unless you like waving goodbye to easy marks!

Vectors

Q1 ABCDE is a pentagon.

$$\overrightarrow{AB} = \begin{pmatrix} 3 \\ 3 \end{pmatrix} \qquad \overrightarrow{AC} = \begin{pmatrix} 2 \\ 6 \end{pmatrix} \qquad \overrightarrow{AD} = \begin{pmatrix} -2 \\ 6 \end{pmatrix} \qquad \overrightarrow{AE} = \begin{pmatrix} -3 \\ 2 \end{pmatrix}$$

a) Draw this pentagon accurately.

b) Write down the vectors:

i) $\overrightarrow{DE}$ ii) $\overrightarrow{DC}$ iii) $\overrightarrow{EC}$

c) What sort of triangle is $\triangle$ ACD?

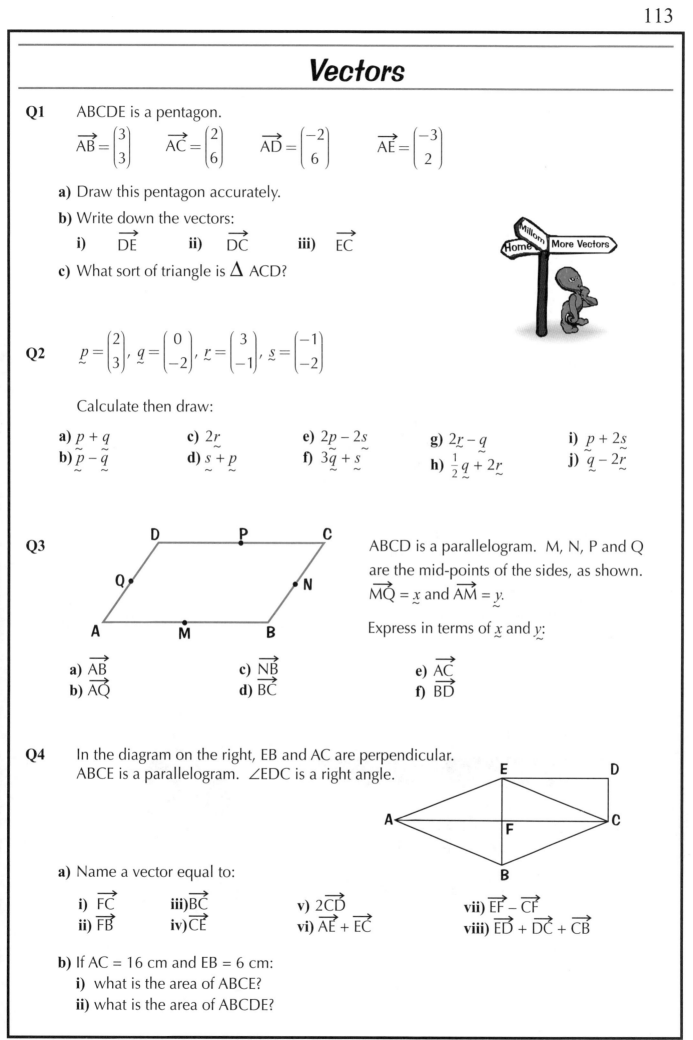

Q2 $\underset{\sim}{p} = \begin{pmatrix} 2 \\ 3 \end{pmatrix}$, $\underset{\sim}{q} = \begin{pmatrix} 0 \\ -2 \end{pmatrix}$, $\underset{\sim}{r} = \begin{pmatrix} 3 \\ -1 \end{pmatrix}$, $\underset{\sim}{s} = \begin{pmatrix} -1 \\ -2 \end{pmatrix}$

Calculate then draw:

a) $p + q$ **c)** $2r$ **e)** $2p - 2s$ **g)** $2\underset{\sim}{r} - q$ **i)** $p + 2s$

b) $\underset{\sim}{p} - \underset{\sim}{q}$ **d)** $\underset{\sim}{s} + \underset{\sim}{p}$ **f)** $3\underset{\sim}{q} + \underset{\sim}{s}$ **h)** $\frac{1}{2}\underset{\sim}{q} + 2\underset{\sim}{r}$ **j)** $\underset{\sim}{q} - 2\underset{\sim}{r}$

Q3

ABCD is a parallelogram. M, N, P and Q are the mid-points of the sides, as shown. $\overrightarrow{MQ} = \underset{\sim}{x}$ and $\overrightarrow{AM} = \underset{\sim}{y}$.

Express in terms of $\underset{\sim}{x}$ and $\underset{\sim}{y}$:

a) $\overrightarrow{AB}$ **c)** $\overrightarrow{NB}$ **e)** $\overrightarrow{AC}$

b) $\overrightarrow{AQ}$ **d)** $\overrightarrow{BC}$ **f)** $\overrightarrow{BD}$

Q4 In the diagram on the right, EB and AC are perpendicular. ABCE is a parallelogram. $\angle EDC$ is a right angle.

a) Name a vector equal to:

i) $\overrightarrow{FC}$ iii) $\overrightarrow{BC}$ v) $2\overrightarrow{CD}$ vii) $\overrightarrow{EF} - \overrightarrow{CF}$

ii) $\overrightarrow{FB}$ iv) $\overrightarrow{CE}$ vi) $\overrightarrow{AE} + \overrightarrow{EC}$ viii) $\overrightarrow{ED} + \overrightarrow{DC} + \overrightarrow{CB}$

b) If AC = 16 cm and EB = 6 cm:

i) what is the area of ABCE?

ii) what is the area of ABCDE?

Probability

If you don't know the **AND** and **OR** rules for multiplying and adding probabilities, you'll be as confused as this duck. For more practice at these sorts of questions see page 93.

Q1 Two friends are taking their piano exams. The probability that Jenna passes is 0.8 and the probability that James passes is 0.3.
   a) Calculate the probability that both Jenna and James pass.
   b) Calculate the probability that neither of them pass.
   c) Calculate the probability that one of them passes, but not both.
   d) What assumption have you made when doing the above calculations?

Q2 In a 200 m swimming race between 8 boys, the probability of Omar winning the race if he is in one of the two outside lanes is 1/4. If he is in any of the other lanes, the probability of Omar winning is 1/3.

   If the lanes are drawn at random, what is the overall probability of Omar winning the race?

Q3 A ball bearing games machine allows balls to drop down chutes. The game is arranged so that the chance of a ball bearing <u>going left</u> at a junction is 3/5. The balls are collected in the cups.

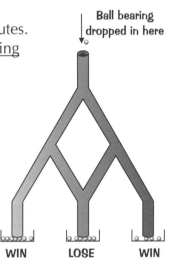
Ball bearing dropped in here

   Lorna is to play the game. Which of the following four statements is <u>true</u>?
   A) The probability of Lorna winning is 2/3.
   B) The probability of Lorna losing is 1 in 3.
   C) The probability of Lorna winning is just slightly greater than 0.5.
   D) The probability of Lorna losing is equal to the probability of Lorna winning.

WIN   LOSE   WIN

Q4 For the roulette wheel shown, the probability of the ball landing on each of the numbers is listed in the table below.

Number	1	2	3	4	5	6
Probability	⅙	⅓	⅙	¹⁄₁₂	¹⁄₁₂	⅙

   a) Find the probability of landing on an even number.
   b) What is the probability of landing on black?
   c) Why is the probability of landing on a white or a 3 not $\frac{5}{12}+\frac{1}{6}$?

Q5 How many times must you roll an ordinary 6-sided dice for the probability of getting at least one 6 to be more than 0.5?

   Don't forget the "<u>at least</u>" trick —
   P(at least 1 six) = 1 – P(no sixes).

Comparing Data

Q1 A dentist is about to employ a dental hygienist. She wishes to know if having a dental hygienist has an <u>effect on the number of fillings</u> she has to perform each year. So, prior to appointing him, the dentist takes some data from the record cards. Here it is:

No. of fillings	0	1	2	3	4	5
No. of children	1	2	8	30	60	12

<u>Three years after</u> appointing the dental hygienist, the dentist takes another set of data from the record cards. Here it is:

No. of fillings	0	1	2	3	4	5
No. of children	11	16	40	32	4	2

See pages 20-21 for more questions on using averages to compare data.

Using any statistical average you need, state what you see from the data, assuming that these records are for <u>new patients</u>.

Q2 The histograms below show the age distributions for two villages — **A** and **B**.

See page 94 for more practice at histogram questions.

Village A

Village B

a) How many people in village **A** are between the ages of 20 and 40?
b) Which village has the larger population?
c) Make one comparison between the distribution of ages in village **A** and village **B**.

Q3 A cat food manufacturer wanted to test two varieties of cat food. 100 cat owners were asked to mark each of the varieties out of 50, based on cat reaction. Here are the results:

Mark	Frequency for variety A	Frequency for variety B
0 < M ≤ 10	5	20
10 < M ≤ 20	5	25
20 < M ≤ 30	20	25
30 < M ≤ 40	60	24
40 < M ≤ 50	10	6

a) Draw a cumulative frequency graph, showing both distributions on the same graph.
b) Use your graph to find the median and interquartile range for each distribution.
c) Use your answers to part **b)** to compare the two distributions.

See page 78-79 for more practice at cumulative frequency questions, and page 80 for more spread of data questions.

Time Series

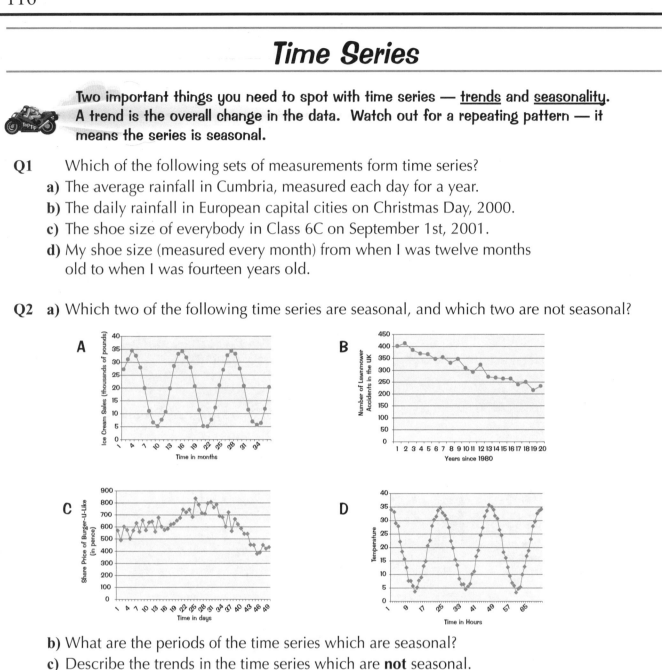

Two important things you need to spot with time series — <u>trends</u> and <u>seasonality</u>. A trend is the overall change in the data. Watch out for a repeating pattern — it means the series is seasonal.

Q1 Which of the following sets of measurements form time series?
a) The average rainfall in Cumbria, measured each day for a year.
b) The daily rainfall in European capital cities on Christmas Day, 2000.
c) The shoe size of everybody in Class 6C on September 1st, 2001.
d) My shoe size (measured every month) from when I was twelve months old to when I was fourteen years old.

Q2 a) Which two of the following time series are seasonal, and which two are not seasonal?

b) What are the periods of the time series which are seasonal?
c) Describe the trends in the time series which are **not** seasonal.

Q3 The following table shows the value of a knitwear company's sock sales in the years 1998-2000. The sales figures are given in thousands of pounds.

Time	Sales
Spring 1998	404
Summer 1998	401
Autumn 1998	411
Winter 1998	420
Spring 1999	416
Summer 1999	409
Autumn 1999	419
Winter 1999	424
Spring 2000	416
Summer 2000	413
Autumn 2000	427
Winter 2000	440

a) Plot the figures on a graph with time on the horizontal axis and sales on the vertical axis.
b) Calculate a 4-point moving average to smooth the series. Copy the table and write your answers in the empty boxes.
c) Plot the moving average on the same axes as your original graph.
d) Describe the trend of the sales figures.

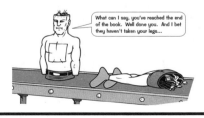

What can I say, you've reached the end of the book. Well done you. And I bet they haven't taken your legs...